Houghton Mifflin
California Math

Homework and Problem Solving

Student Book

- **Homework**
- **Leveled Problem Solving**

Visit **Education Place**
www.eduplace.com/kids

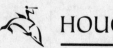

HOUGHTON MIFFLIN

BOSTON

Printed in the U.S.A.

ISBN 10: 0-618-96128-3
ISBN 13: 978-0-618-96128-3

        13   0982   16 15 14 13 12
4500361137

Hands On: Model Numbers

CA Standard
KEY NS 1.3

Draw a quick picture to model 135.

hundreds   tens   ones

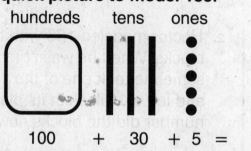

100   +   30   + 5   =   135

Draw a quick picture to model each number.

1. 145

2. 223

3. 301

4. 179

Spiral Review (Grade 2, Chapter 17, Lesson 1) **KEY NS 4.1**

Write >, <, or = for each.

5. $\frac{3}{12}$ ◯ $\frac{1}{4}$

6. $\frac{1}{7}$ ◯ $\frac{1}{3}$

7. Write true or false. One-sixth of a pizza is greater than one-eighth.

_____

Hands On: Model Numbers

CA Standard
KEY NS 1.3

Solve.

1. Cassie has the base-ten blocks shown below. She wants to model 244. What does she need to get?

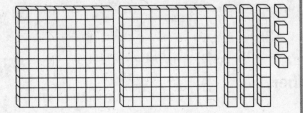

2. Hector modeled 138 with base-ten blocks. When he wasn't looking, someone took one of the 10-blocks and left a 1-block in its place. What number did the blocks now model?

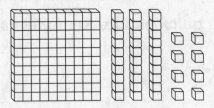

3. Deshawn has five base-ten blocks. She models a number that is less than 999. The number she models has a zero in the tens place and a zero in the ones place. What number is she modeling?

4. Greg has the same number of 1-blocks, 10-blocks, and 100-blocks. He models an even number that is less than 400. What is the number?

5. Kwan has modeled a number that is less than 999. His model has twice as many 100-blocks as 10-blocks. It has twice as many 10-blocks as 1-blocks. What is the number?

6. Shoshanna is going to use 12 base-ten blocks to model the largest possible number less than 999. Then she will use another 12 blocks to model the smallest possible number less than 999. What are the two numbers?

Place Value Through 999

CA Standards
KEY NS 1.3, **KEY** NS 1.5

hundreds	tens	ones
2	5	3

The value of the 2 is 200.

The value of the 5 is 50.

The value of the 3 is 3.

There are different ways to write a number.

Use expanded form.	Use standard form.	Use word form.
200 + 50 + 3	253	two hundred fifty-three

Write each number in standard form.

1. _____

2. 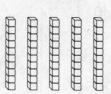 _____

Find the value of .

3. 100 + 50 + ☐ = 153 _____

4. 200 + ☐ + 7 = 267 _____

Spiral Review (Grade 2, Chapter 4, Lessons 2–3) **KEY** NS 1.3, NS 1.1

Compare the numbers. Write <, >, or =.

5. 84 ◯ 56

6. 135 ◯ 142

7. Kim read for 43 minutes. Sam read for 51 minutes. Alice read for 49 minutes. Which one read for the greatest number of minutes?

Place Value Through 999

CA Standards
NS 1.3, **KEY** NS 1.5

Use the table to solve Problems 1–4.

There have been a total of 6 missions in which astronauts landed on the moon. The length of each of those missions is shown in the table below.

1. In 1969, the Apollo 11 astronauts became the first people to land on the moon. How would you write the number of hours for their mission in expanded form? In word form?

_____

_____

Time in Outer Space	
Mission	**Hours**
Apollo 11	195 hours
Apollo 12	245 hours
Apollo 14	216 hours
Apollo 15	295 hours
Apollo 16	266 hours
Apollo 17	302 hours

2. Which mission's length has the same digit in the tens place and the ones place?

_____

3. The length of my Apollo mission is an odd 3-digit number. The digit in the tens place is twice the hundreds digit. On which Apollo mission did I serve?

_____

4. Ken says that the *Apollo 14* mission was in outer space for about 200 hours. Bill says it was in outer space for about 300 hours. Who do you think is correct? Explain your choice.

_____

_____

5. What is the greatest possible number that has an expanded form containing just one zero?

_____

6. How many numbers from 1 to 200 have an expanded form that is identical to the standard form? What are they?

_____

_____

_____

Hands On: How Big Is 1,000?

Step 1 Color a row of 10 squares on grid paper. Then color 9 more rows below the first row.

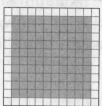

Step 2 Look at your model. How many squares did you color in all?

Think: How many rows did you color? How many squares did you color in each row?

Write your answer in the first row of the table.

Step 3 Repeat Step 1 so you have 2 models of 100. How many colored squares are in 2 models of 100? Write your answer in the second row of the table.

Step 4 Repeat Step 1 eight more times so you have 10 models of 100. Then complete the table.

Number of Models	Number of Squares
1	
2	
3	
4	
5	
6	
7	
8	
9	
10	

Tell if each is *greater than*, *less than*, or *equal to* 1,000.

1. 10 boxes of 10 envelopes _____

2. 10 bags of 100 push pins _____

3. 8 bags of 100 buttons _____

4. 1 pack of 1,000 sheets of paper _____

Spiral Review (Grade 2, Chapter 13, Lesson 4) **NS 5.2**

Find the sum.

5. 2 dimes, 10 nickels, 6 quarters, 3 half-dollars, and 1 five-dollar bill. _____

6. $17.34 + $5.99 _____

7. Julie wants to buy an eraser, a pack of pencils, and a ruler from the supply shop. The cashier says her total is $5.00. She puts 2 one-dollar bills, 5 quarters, 7 dimes on the counter. How much more money does she need to buy her items?

_____

Hands On: How Big Is 1,000?

CA Standards
NS 1.1, NS 1.0

The Space Museum store sells glow-in-the-dark star stickers in the packages shown below. For Problems 1–5, tell if each person bought *more than 1,000, less than 1,000,* or *exactly 1,000* star stickers.

1. Tim bought 5 rolls of star stickers.

   _____

2. Carol bought 9 boxes of star stickers.

   _____

3. Anita bought 10 rolls and 5 packs of star stickers.

   _____

4. Jamal bought 10 sheets and one roll of star stickers.

   _____

5. Jonah bought 4 rolls, 58 sheets, and 20 packs of star stickers.

   _____

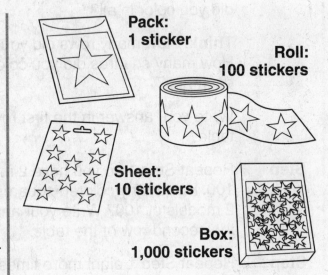

Pack:
1 sticker

Roll:
100 stickers

Sheet:
10 stickers

Box:
1,000 stickers

6. Kelly wants to put 1,000 star stickers on her bedroom ceiling. If Kelly got 5 rolls of star stickers for her birthday, how many more stickers would she need to buy? How many more rolls of stickers would she need to buy? How many more sheets of stickers?

   _____

   _____

Place Value to 10,000

CA Standards
KEY NS 1.3, KEY NS 1.5

thousands	hundreds	tens	ones
1	2	3	1

The value of the 1 is 1000.

The value of the 2 is 200.

The value of the 3 is 30.

The value of the 1 is 1.

Different Ways to Write a Number		
You can use expanded form.	**You can use standard form.**	**You can use word form.**
$1,000 + 200 + 30 + 1$	1,231 A comma is used to separate thousands and hundreds.	one thousand, two hundred thirty-one

Write the place of the underlined digit. Then write its value.

1. 2,8<u>4</u>6

2. <u>5</u>,719

Write each number in expanded form.

3. 4,328

4. 6,135

Spiral Review (Grade 2, Chapter 20, Lessons 2–4) **KEY NS 3.1, KEY NS 3.0**

5. $7 \times 5 =$ ☐

6. $10 \times 6 =$ ☐

7. Anna has filled 5 pages of a photo album. Each page holds 4 photos. How many pictures are in Anna's photo album?

Place Value to 10,000

CA Standards
KEY NS 1.3, KEY NS 1.5

Scientists describe the size of a planet or a moon by its diameter, or the distance through its middle. The table below shows the diameters of the largest moons in our solar system and the planet that each moon orbits.

Moon Sizes		
Moon	**Planet**	**Diameter**
Callisto	Jupiter	2,984 miles
Europa	Jupiter	1,944 miles
Ganymede	Jupiter	3,272 miles
Io	Jupiter	2,262 miles
Moon	Earth	2,160 miles
Titan	Saturn	3,198 miles
Triton	Neptune	1,680 miles

1. Which moons have diameters less than two thousand miles long?

2. Which moons' diameters have a 2 in the hundreds place?

3. I am one of Jupiter's moons. My diameter does not have a 2 in the thousands place. The digit in the tens place is the same as the ones digit. Which moon am I?

4. Suppose a moon in another solar system has a diameter greater than Triton's and less than Europa's. How many different digits could the diameter have in the hundreds place? What are they?

5. If for each moon you switched the thousands digit with the hundreds digit, I would have the largest diameter. Which moon am I?

6. Allison added the diameters of three moons. She got a total that had a 0 in the ones place. One of these was Triton. Which other moon had to be in the group?

Problem Solving: Number Patterns

CA Standards
MR 1.1, AF 2.2

Elaine is making goody bags for her birthday party. Each bag contains 7 different treats. How many treats will she need to fill 8 goody bags?

Step 1 Note that the number pattern is count by 7s, or +7.

Step 2 Count by 7s to find the number of treats in the goody bags.

bags	1 bag	2 bags	3 bags	4 bags	5 bags	6 bags	7 bags	8 bags
treats	7 treats	14 treats	21 treats	28 treats	35 treats	42 treats	49 treats	56 treats

Solution: There are 56 treats in 8 goody bags.

Find the number pattern to solve each problem.

1. Elaine's birthday cake has 8 candles on it. If she had 10 birthday cakes, how many candles would they have in all?

   _____

2. Elaine received 7 gifts in wrapped boxes. Each box had 6 stickers on it. How many stickers were there on all 7 boxes?

   _____

3. Elaine made special place mats for her party. She drew 5 stars on each place mat. How many stars were on 8 place mats?

   _____

4. The first four houses on Elaine's street are numbered 215, 225, 235, and 245. If the number pattern continues, what are the numbers on the next two houses likely to be?

   _____

Problem Solving: Number Patterns

CA Standards
MR 1.1, AF 2.2

Solve each problem.

1. During leap years, one extra day is added to the year. In the 21st century, the first four leap years are 2000, 2004, 2008, and 2012. Following this pattern, what will be the fifth leap year in the new century?

_____

2. Phil made calendars for his friend. Each calendar had 12 pages, one for each month. How many pages did he make if he made 4 calendars?

_____

3. David is making a beaded necklace. He has used 11 red beads, 9 orange beads, and 7 yellow beads. He wants to continue the pattern with white beads. How many white beads is he likely to use?

_____

4. Diane made silver bracelets for members of her family. Each bracelet took her 30 minutes to make. If she spent 3 hours making bracelets, how many members of her family did she make bracelets for?

_____

5. The first four tables at a craft show are numbered 13, 15, 18, and 22. If the pattern continues, what are the next two table numbers likely to be?

_____

6. A craft sampler includes a bag of colored beads, 2 lengths of wire for a necklace or bracelet, a small container of glue, and a leather pouch. What is the total number of items in 12 samplers?

_____

Name _____ Date _____

Hands On: Compare Numbers

CA Standards
NS 1.2, **KEY** NS 1.3

Compare using a place-value chart base-10 blocks.

115 ◯ 143

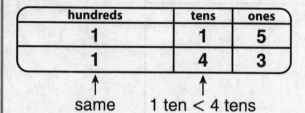

hundreds	tens	ones
1	1	5
1	4	3

↑ same   ↑ 1 ten < 4 tens

So, 115 < 143.

Compare. Write >, <, or = for each ◯.

1. 37 ◯ 32   **2.** 48 ◯ 78   **3.** 93 ◯ 93   **4.** 8 ◯ 80

5. 129 ◯ 93   **6.** 1,645 ◯ 1,643   **7.** 705 ◯ 792   **8.** 1,586 ◯ 1,986

Write = or ≠ for each ◯.

9. 12 + 4 ◯ 18   **10.** 15 + 4 ◯ 19   **11.** 20 + 3 ◯ 23

12. 40 + 6 ◯ 64   **13.** 100 + 40 ◯ 130   **14.** 200 + 3 ◯ 230

Spiral Review (Chapter 1, Lesson 1) **KEY** NS 1.3

For 15–16, write the value of the underlined digit.

15. <u>8</u>04 _____   **16.** 2<u>7</u>1 _____

17. Claudi says that the value of the underlined digit in 1<u>0</u>3 is 0.
Is she correct? Why or why not?

_____

_____

Hands On: Compare Numbers

CA Standards
NS 1.2, KEY NS 1.3

Use the table to answer the questions.

Enrollment in a Music School	
Instrument	**Number of Students**
Clarinet	108
Flute	119
French Horn	56
Guitar	123
Drums	112
Piano	121
Saxophone	110
Trumpet	114
Tuba	73
Violin	116

1. Which instrument are more students studying, piano or violin?

_____

2. Which instrument are fewer students studying, saxophone or flute?

_____

3. Which instruments are more students studying than flute?

_____

_____

4. Which are the three *least* popular instruments?

_____

_____

5. Which instruments have more than 114 students enrolled?

_____

_____

6. How many students would need to switch from violin to clarinet for there to be more clarinet students than violin students?

_____

_____

Name _____ Date _____

Order Numbers to 10,000

CA Standards
NS 1.2, **KEY** NS 1.3

Karin spent her summer at a performing arts camp. She was one of 175 campers in the group studying singing. There were 241 campers in the dancing group and 192 in the acting group. Which group had the least number of campers?

The order of the numbers from least to greatest is: 175 192 241

Solution: The group studying singing had the least number of campers.

hundreds	tens	ones
1	7	5
2	4	1
1	9	2

↑ 1 hundred < 2 hundreds, so 241 is the greatest number.

↑ 7 tens < 9 tens, so 175 is the least number.

Write the numbers in order from least to greatest.

1. 18   23   14

_____

2. 127   98   125

_____

3. 2,367   2,514   1,879

_____

4. 89   879   409

_____

5. 115   521   512

_____

6. 6,495   6,395   6,459

_____

Write the numbers in order from greatest to least.

7. 73   71   80

_____

8. 497   492   536

_____

9. 972   1,583   1,246

_____

10. 185   105   1,058

_____

11. 237   1,717   1,770

_____

12. 9,999   9,799   998

_____

Spiral Review (Chapter 1, Lesson 2) **KEY** NS 1.3, **KEY** NS 1.5

Find the value of □.

13. $300 + 80 + □ = 384$ _____

14. $500 + □ + 6 = 516$ _____

15. I am a number greater than 99 and less than 1,000. Two of my digits that aren't next to each other are the same. My tens digit could not be greater and it is 1 more than my hundreds digit. What number am I?

_____

Name _____ Date _____

Order Numbers to 10,000

Use the table below for Problems 1–4.

1. Order the number of tickets sold for each play from least to greatest.

_____

2. Which play had the greatest number of tickets sold? Which had the least?

_____

Shakespeare Festival Ticket Sales	
Play	Number of Tickets
Hamlet	496
Macbeth	512
Romeo and Juliet	469
Othello	460

3. **What If?** Suppose ten more tickets were sold for *Othello*. Would this affect your answer for Problem 2? Explain your thinking.

_____

_____

_____

4. **You Decide** Emma says that she does not have to compare the digits in the ones place to solve Problem 2. Do you agree? Explain your answer.

_____

_____

_____

_____

Use the table below for Problems 5–6.

5. Order the number of lines from greatest to least for the plays *Coriolanus, Cymbeline*, and *Richard III*.

_____

6. How do the numbers in the answer to Problem 5 differ from the other two numbers in the table?

_____

Shakespeare's Longest Plays	
Play	Number of Lines
Coriolanus	3,820
Cymbeline	3,813
Hamlet	3,901
Othello	3,672
Richard III	3,886

Round 2-Digit and 3-Digit Numbers

CA Standards
NS 1.4, NS 1.0

You can round a larger number to the nearest ten or the nearest hundred.

Round 376 to the nearest ten.

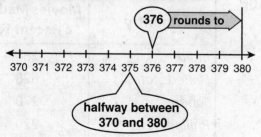

So 376 rounded to the nearest ten is **380**.

Round 376 to the nearest hundred.

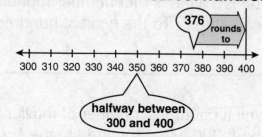

So 376 rounded to the nearest hundred is **400**.

**For each number, write the 2 tens the number is between.
Then round to the nearest ten.**

1. 21   **2.** 76   **3.** 483   **4.** 625

_____   _____   _____   _____

**For each number, write the 2 hundreds the number is between.
Then round to the nearest hundred.**

5. 361   **6.** 537   **7.** 258   **8.** 709

_____   _____   _____   _____

Spiral Review (Chapter 1, Lesson 4) NS 1.1, **KEY** NS 1.3, **KEY** NS 1.5

Write the place of the underlined digit. Then write its value.

9. 3,7̲04 _____   **10.** 6̲,249 _____

11. Paul is thinking of the largest possible 4-digit number that
has four different digits. What is the number?

_____

Name _____ Date _____

Round 2-Digit and 3-Digit Numbers

Use the table to solve.

Countries That Make the Most Movies	
Country	Movies Made in a Recent Year
India	764
United States	628
Japan	270
Philippines	220
France	181
Hong Kong	146
Italy	108
Spain	97
United Kingdom	92
China	85

1. How many movies were made in the United States? What is that number rounded to the nearest ten? To the nearest hundred?

   _____

2. Which countries' number of movies are about 200 when rounded to the nearest hundred?

   _____

   _____

3. Which countries' number of movies seem to be already rounded to the nearest ten? Why might someone think this?

   _____

   _____

4. **Reasoning** When my number of movies is rounded to the nearest ten, it is 50 more than my number of movies rounded to the nearest hundred. What country am I?

   _____

   _____

5. **Write About It** When rounded to the nearest ten, a number is 100. Does this mean that the original number must be a three-digit number? Use one of the numbers in the table to explain your answer.

   _____

   _____

6. How useful would a bar chart be if it showed all the movie data rounded to the nearest hundred? Explain your answer.

   _____

   _____

Round 4-Digit Numbers

CA Standards
NS 1.4, NS 1.0

Round 4,376 to the place of the underlined digit.

Use a Number Line

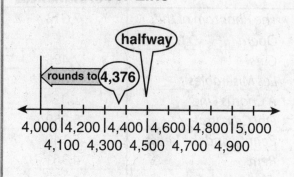

Use rounding rules.

Circle the digit to the right of the underlined digit.

4,③76
↑

If the circled digit is 5 or greater, round up.

If the circled digit is less than 5, round down.

4,③76   3 < 5, so
↓   round down
4, 000

Round to the place of the underlined digit.

1. 2,634   2. 4,258   3. 1,597   4. 381   5. 4,965

_____   _____   _____   _____   _____

6. 7,821   7. 2,358   8. 9,191   9. 6,435   10. 891

_____   _____   _____   _____   _____

Spiral Review   (Chapter 2, Lesson 2) **NS 1.2, KEY NS 1.3**

Write the numbers in the order indicated.

11. least to greatest
    432   485   443   413

12. greatest to least
    6,988   7,560   6,857   7,554

_____   _____

13. Listed below are the last names of four U.S. presidents and the year each one was elected. Write the names in the order they served as president.

    Grant 1868   Coolidge 1922   Wilson 1912   Buchanan 1856

_____

Round 4-Digit Numbers

Use the table to solve.

1. What is the longest-running Broadway show? Rounded to the nearest hundred, how many times was the show performed?

   _____

   _____

Longest-Running Broadway Shows*	
Show	Number of Performances
The Phantom of the Opera	7,813
Cats	7,485
Les Misérables	6,680
A Chorus Line	6,137
Oh! Calcutta!	5,959
Beauty and the Beast	5,140
Rent	4,361
Chicago	4,139
Miss Saigon	4,092
The Lion King	3,723

*as of November, 2006

2. Rounded to the nearest thousand, which shows were performed about 6,000 times?

   _____

   _____

3. Which two shows have the same number of performances when rounded to the nearest thousand **and** when rounded to the nearest hundred?

   _____

   _____

4. **Reasoning** When rounded to the nearest ten, my number of performances ends in the digits 90. I am not *Miss Saigon*. What show am I?

   _____

   _____

5. The answer is *four* of the shows. What question about the data in the table could have been asked?

   _____

   _____

6. Suppose you are making a pictogram of the data in the table and you don't want any row to have more than 10 pictures in it. How many performances should each picture represent? How many rows would contain a half-picture?

   _____

   _____

Name _____ Date _____

Addition with Regrouping

CA Standards
KEY NS 2.1, MR 2.3

Rosa's class made 127 programs for the class play. The class also made 149 programs for music night. How many programs did the class make in all?

You can add numbers by using columns. First add the ones, then the tens, then the hundreds.

Add.

If the sum of the digits in the ones place is 10 or greater, regroup 10 ones as 1 ten. Then add the tens.

$$
\begin{array}{r}
1 \\
127 \\
+149 \\
\hline
276
\end{array}
$$

Solution: The class made 276 programs in all.

Find the sum.

1. $\begin{array}{r}175\\+118\\\hline\end{array}$	2. $\begin{array}{r}329\\+164\\\hline\end{array}$	3. $\begin{array}{r}257\\+124\\\hline\end{array}$	4. $\begin{array}{r}36\\+49\\\hline\end{array}$	5. $\begin{array}{r}408\\+387\\\hline\end{array}$
6. $\begin{array}{r}127\\+236\\\hline\end{array}$	7. $\begin{array}{r}28\\+59\\\hline\end{array}$	8. $\begin{array}{r}308\\+246\\\hline\end{array}$	9. $\begin{array}{r}165\\+417\\\hline\end{array}$	10. $\begin{array}{r}249\\+439\\\hline\end{array}$

Spiral Review (Chapter 1, Lesson 2) **KEY** NS 1.3, **KEY** NS 1.5

Find the value of ☐.

11. $700 + \boxed{} + 7 = 737$ 12. $5,000 + \boxed{} + 9 = 5,019$

13. Marcy is writing a report for her History class. She counts 3,587 words in her report. Which digit holds the thousands place of her word count?

_____

Homework and Problem Solving
19
Use with text pp. 50–51

Hands On: Addition with Regrouping

Use the table to solve the problems.

Threatened and Endangered Animals in the United States		
Animal Group	Number Threatened	Number Endangered
Mammals	9	65
Birds	14	78
Reptiles	22	14
Amphibians	9	12
Fish	44	71
Clams	8	62
Snails	11	21
Insects	9	35
Arachnids	0	12
Crustaceans	3	18

1. How many mammals in the United States are classified as threatened or endangered?

2. How many threatened or endangered insects are there in the United States?

3. Clams, snails, and crustaceans all have shells. One of these groups of animals has more than 50 endangered or threatened species in all. Which group is it?

4. Which group has the most threatened or endangered animals?

5. Arachnids include spiders, mites, and ticks. Arachnids are different from insects because they have 8 legs. But Vito calls all the animals in both groups "bugs." How many threatened or endangered animals are in Vito's "bug" group?

6. Clams and fish have 0 feet. Snails have 1 foot. Birds have 2 feet. Which group has the most endangered or threatened animals: clams and fish, snails, or birds?

Equations and Inequalities

CA Standard
KEY AF 1.1

In an equation, both expressions have the **same** value. In an inequality, the expressions have **different** values.

Is this an equation or an inequality? $13 + 12$ ☐ $20 + 4$ $13 + 12 = 25$ $20 + 4 = 24$ The expressions have different values, so it is an inequality. Write $>$ in the box to show that 25 is more than 24. **Solution:** inequality	Is this an equation or an inequality? $6 + 5 + 11$ ☐ $3 + 4 + 15$ $6 + 5 + 11 = 22$ $3 + 4 + 15 = 22$ The expressions have the same value, so it is an equation. Write $=$ in the box. **Solution:** equation

Write $>$, $<$, or $=$ in each ☐ **to make the number sentence true.**

1. $9 + 5 + 20$ ☐ $17 + 17$ **2.** $16 + 22$ ☐ $5 + 18 + 16$

3. $26 + 19$ ☐ $37 + 7$

Write a number in the ☐ **that makes the number sentence true.**

4. $51 +$ ☐ $< 16 + 73$ **5.** $7 + 42 >$ ☐ $+ 26$ **6.** ☐ $+ 33 = 5 + 40$

Spiral Review (Chapter 2, Lesson 2) **NS 1.2, KEY NS 1.3**

7. Write the numbers in order from least to greatest.

77 67 76 _____

8. Write the numbers in order from greatest to least.

112 111 121 _____

9. One beanbag has 143 beans. Another beanbag has 133 beans. A third beanbag has 134 beans. Which bag has the fewest beans?

_____

Equations and Inequalities

**CA Standard
KEY AF 1.1**

**In Problems 1–4, read each story. Write the equation
or inequality that matches the story.**

1. There are 14 black ducks and 7 white
ducks swimming in the pond. There
are 20 black ducks and 2 white ducks
sitting on the grass. Compare the
number of ducks swimming to the
number of ducks sitting.

_____

2. In the barn, 13 cows are eating
and 18 cows are sleeping. Outside,
29 cows are standing and 2 cows
are sitting. Compare the number of
cows in the barn to the number of
cows outside.

_____

3. In the east half of the desert, there
are 368 orchid cactus and 137
golden ball cactus. In the west half
of the desert, there are 150 orchid
cactus, 263 golden ball cactus, and
91 hedgehog cactus. Compare the
number of cactus in the east to the
number of cactus in the west.

_____

_____

4. Oscar Otter swam in the river for
9 hours on Monday, 15 hours on
Tuesday, 6 hours on Wednesday, 12
hours on Thursday, and 12 hours on
Friday. Ollie Otter swam for 10 hours
on Monday, 13 hours on Tuesday,
14 hours on Wednesday, 17 hours
on Thursday, and 0 hours on Friday.
Compare the number of hours Oscar
swam to the number of hours Ollie
swam.

_____

_____

Write a short story about animals to match the inequality or equation.

5. $18 + 26 > 23 + 14$

_____

_____

_____

_____

_____

6. $23 + 9 = 10 + 22$

_____

_____

_____

_____

_____

Addition Properties

CA Standards
KEY NS 2.1, AF 1.0

Commutative Property

You can change the order of numbers when you add, and the sum will not change.

$$8 + 12 = 20 \qquad 12 + 8 = 20$$

Zero Property

When you add a number and zero, the sum is that number.

$$13 + 0 = 13$$

Associative Property

When you group numbers to add, how you group them does not change the sum.

$$(3 + 5) + 2 \qquad\qquad 3 + (5 + 2)$$
$$8 + 2 = 10 \qquad\qquad 3 + 7 = 10$$

Find the sum.

1. $3 + 7 =$ _____

   $7 + 3 =$ _____

2. $8 + 4 =$ _____

   $4 + 8 =$ _____

3. $5 + 9 =$ _____

   $9 + 5 =$ _____

4. $2 + 0 =$ _____

5. $0 + 5 =$ _____

6. $0 + 7 =$ _____

7. $4 + (8 + 5) =$ _____

8. $(1 + 9) + 5 =$ _____

9. $4 + (8 + 5) =$ _____

Spiral Review (Chapter 1, Lesson 4) NS 1.1, **KEY** NS 1.3, **KEY** NS 1.5

10. How many hundreds are there in 6,703? _____

11. What is the place of the underlined digit in 1,3$\underline{2}$8? _____

12. I have a 9 in the hundreds place. I have a 6 in the ones place. I have a 5 in the thousands place. I have a 4 in the tens place. What number am I?

_____

Addition Properties

Use addition properties to answer each question about national parks.

1. There are 5 national parks in Louisiana. Mississippi has 7 national parks. Alabama has 5 national parks. Think about adding those three numbers. Which two numbers would you add first? Why?

_____

_____

2. Alaska has 18 national parks. If you add zero to that number, you get the number of national parks in Virginia. How many national parks are in Virginia? How do you know?

_____

_____

3. Kai likes caves. He spent 45 minutes in Wind Cave, 57 minutes in Mammoth Cave, and 60 minutes in Carlsbad Caverns. How long did he spend in the caves in all?

_____

4. Mindy went camping at Redwood National Park. She got 16 mosquito bites on Friday, 0 bites on Saturday, 7 bites on Sunday, and 24 bites on Monday. How many mosquito bites did Mindy get altogether?

_____

5. California has more national parks than many other states. The sum of the two digits in its number of parks is 6. Both digits are even. If California has fewer than 30 national parks, how many does it have?

_____

6. At Channel Islands, Sally Sea Lion slept in the sun seventy-seven hours one week, sixty-six hours the next week, seventy hours the third week, and sixty-two hours the fourth week. Sheldon Sea Lion slept seventy hours, sixty-two hours, seventy-seven hours, and sixty-six hours. Who slept more?

_____

Column Addition

CA Standards
KEY NS 2.1, MR 2.2

The auditorium has 214 seats on the first level, 59 seats on the second level, and 76 seats on the third level. How many seats does the auditorium have?

Find 214 + 59 + 76.

```
  11
 214
  59
+ 76
─────
 349
```

Solution: The auditorium has 349 seats.

Add.

1.
```
 125
  64
+  3
```

2.
```
  82
  29
+ 53
```

3.
```
 316
  57
+ 34
```

4.
```
  35
  97
+503
```

5.
```
 498
  67
+213
```

6.
```
  79
 344
+476
```

7.
```
 194
 604
+ 96
```

8.
```
 203
  57
+578
```

9.
```
 589
 207
+ 46
```

10.
```
 415
 501
+ 34
```

Spiral Review (Chapter 2, Lesson 2) **NS 1.2, KEY NS 1.3**

11. Write the numbers in order from least to greatest: 199, 191, 991. _____

12. Write the numbers in order from greatest to least: 3,422; 3,424; 3,222.

_____

13. In one year, Carlo Chuckwalla ate 413 cactus flowers. Claire Chuckwalla ate 314 cactus flowers. Chuck Chuckwalla ate 343 cactus flowers. List the Chuckwallas in order from who ate the most to who ate the fewest cactus flowers.

_____

Column Addition

CA Standards
KEY NS 2.1, MR 2.2

Answer each question about animals.

1. A greyhound can run 39 miles per hour. A gazelle can run 11 miles per hour faster than a greyhound. A cheetah can run 20 miles per hour faster than a gazelle. How fast can a cheetah run?

2. California sea lion pups weigh about 16 pounds. The mother weighs about 160 pounds more than her pup. The father weighs about 485 pounds more than the mother. How much does an adult male sea lion usually weigh?

3. The average third grader has 20 teeth. A polar bear has 22 more teeth than a third grader, and an orca whale has 6 more teeth than a polar bear. A crocodile has 8 more teeth than an orca. How many teeth does a crocodile have?

4. Most giraffes have a tail that is 36 inches long. A leopard's tail is usually 3 inches shorter than a giraffe's tail. An Asian elephant's tail is 5 inches longer than a leopard's tail. How long is the elephant's tail?

5. A whale shark can be 58 feet long and it can weigh 7,000 pounds. A pygmy shark is usually only 2 feet long. In between are the great white shark at 21 feet, the hammerhead at 15 feet, and the basking shark at 40 feet. If you line up these five sharks, how many feet long will the line be?

6. There are 2,700 species of snakes. A coral snake is 30 inches long. A copperhead is 18 inches longer. A king snake is 12 inches longer than a copperhead. A boa is 108 inches longer than a king snake. A python is the longest—192 inches longer than a boa. How long is a python?

Add Greater Numbers

CA Standards
KEY NS 2.1, AF 1.0

In the town of Harville, there are 2,348 people. In the town of Oakdale, there are 1,976 people. How many people are there in both towns combined?

Add 2,348 + 1,976.

For each place, you should regroup if the sum of the digits in the column is 10 or greater.

```
 1 1 1
  2,348
+ 1,976
  4,324
```

Solution: There are 4,324 people in both towns combined.

Find the sum.

1. 2,356
   + 1,968

2. 1,872
   + 3,569

3. 3,079
   + 2,975

4. 6,569
   + 2,434

5. 4,897
   + 3,844

6. 2,796
   + 5,895

7. 1,480
   + 2,320

8. 8,961
   + 3,425

Spiral Review (Chapter 2, Lesson 3) **NS 1.4, NS 1.0**

9. Round 261 to the nearest ten. _____

10. Round 261 to the nearest hundred. _____

11. Riverside Elementary School has 579 students. How many students is this to the nearest ten?

_____

Add Greater Numbers

CA Standards
KEY NS 2.1, AF 1.0

Use the table to solve.

Largest Saltwater Fish Caught	
Fish	**Weight**
Atlantic blue marlin	1,402 pounds
Black marlin	1,560 pounds
Bluefin tuna	1,496 pounds
Great white shark	2,664 pounds
Greenland shark	1,709 pounds
Pacific blue marlin	1,376 pounds
Shortfin mako shark	1,221 pounds
Swordfish	1,182 pounds
Tiger shark	1,780 pounds

1. How much do the tiger shark and the black marlin weigh together?

2. How much do the Greenland shark and the Atlantic blue marlin weigh together?

3. Which two fish in the table weigh the least? What is their combined weight?

4. Find the two fish in the table that weigh the most. How much do those two fish weigh together?

5. Someone catches a tiger shark that weighs 4,817 pounds more than the largest one caught before. How much does this tiger shark weigh?

6. Which two fish together weigh 2,872 pounds?

Hands On: Model Subtraction

CA Standards
KEY NS 2.1, MR 2.3

Find 654 − 238.

$$\begin{array}{r} \overset{414}{6\cancel{5}4} \\ -238 \\ \hline 416 \end{array}$$

Check:

$$\begin{array}{rl} 654 & \text{rounds to} \\ -238 & \text{rounds to} \\ \end{array} \quad \begin{array}{r} 700 \\ -200 \\ \hline 500 \end{array}$$

654 − 238 = 416

Find each difference. Estimate to check.

1. $\begin{array}{r} 33 \\ -17 \\ \hline \end{array}$

2. $\begin{array}{r} 72 \\ -25 \\ \hline \end{array}$

3. $\begin{array}{r} \$60 \\ -\$15 \\ \hline \end{array}$

4. $\begin{array}{r} 33 \\ -18 \\ \hline \end{array}$

5. $\begin{array}{r} 81 \\ -68 \\ \hline \end{array}$

6. $\begin{array}{r} 434 \\ -118 \\ \hline \end{array}$

7. $\begin{array}{r} 225 \\ -118 \\ \hline \end{array}$

8. $\begin{array}{r} 150 \\ -\ 82 \\ \hline \end{array}$

9. $\begin{array}{r} \$392 \\ -\$149 \\ \hline \end{array}$

10. $\begin{array}{r} 745 \\ -318 \\ \hline \end{array}$

11. 94 − 57 = _____

12. $671 − $216 = _____

13. 843 − 527 = _____

14. $391 − $119 = _____

Spiral Review (Chapter 3, Lesson 3) **KEY** NS 2.1, AF 1.0

For 15 and 16 write the number that makes the number sentence true. Tell which property of addition you used.

15. 5 + 8 = _____ + 5

16. (7 + _____) + 2 = 7 + (4 + 2)

_____

_____

17. It took Aram 15 minutes to bicycle to the library. If you add
0 to that number, you get the number of minutes Aram
spent in the library. How many minutes did Aram
spend in the library?

_____

Model Subtraction

CA Standards
KEY NS 2.1, MR 2.3

Use the table to solve. Show your work.

1. How many miles longer is New York's subway than Chicago's subway?

   _____

2. Which city's subway has more stations, Berlin or Mexico City? How many more stations?

   _____

3. In which two cities do the subways have about 150 stations? Which of those cities has the longer subway? How much longer?

   _____

   _____

World's Longest Subways		
City	**Number of Stations**	**Number of Miles**
Berlin	170	90
Chicago	143	222
Copenhagen	22	14
London	275	253
Mexico City	150	111
Moscow	175	149
New York	468	656
Paris	368	124
Seoul	115	94
Tokyo	148	183

4. Seoul is the capital of South Korea. Tokyo is the capital of Japan. Which of these Asian capital cities has the longer subway? How much longer?

   _____

5. If this city added 404 more miles to its subway, it would have the longest subway in the world. What city is it?

   _____

6. The combined subway miles of London and another city is 254 miles less than the miles of subways in New York. What is the other city?

   _____

Hands On: Subtract with Regrouping

CA Standard
KEY NS 2.1

Find 612 − 384.

Regroup from greater places as needed.

```
    10
  5 Ø12
  61̸2̸                228
  −384    Check   +384
  228              612
```

Solution: 612 − 384 = 228

Subtract. Check using addition.

1. 361
    −148

2. 719
    −432

3. 471
    −275

4. 577
    −159

5. 721
    −163

6. 518
    −188

7. 342
    −146

8. 927
    −719

9. 856
    −475

10. 323
    −277

11. 472
    −180

12. 642
    −173

13. 425 − 172 =

14. 681 − 483 =

15. 537 − 364 =

16. 934 − 379 =

_____   _____   _____   _____

Spiral Review   (Chapter 2, Lesson 4) **NS 1.4, NS 1.0**

Solve.

17. What is 4,592 rounded to the nearest thousand?

_____

18. What is 6,652 rounded to the nearest ten?

_____

19. The Tran family drove 1,584 miles from Paso Robles, California, to visit relatives in Austin, Texas. About how many miles is that, rounded to the nearest hundred?

_____

Name _____ Date _____

Hands On: Subtract with Regrouping

Use the map showing driving distances in miles to answer the problems.

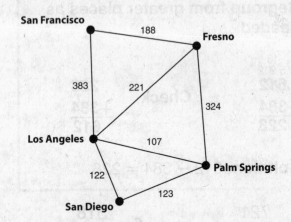

1. How many more miles is it from San Francisco to Los Angeles than from Los Angeles to San Diego?

   _____

2. How many fewer miles is it from Palm Springs to Los Angeles than from Palm Springs to Fresno?

   _____

3. What is the greatest number of cities you can drive to if you start from any city and drive less than 600 miles? Describe the route.

   _____

   _____

   _____

4. How many miles difference is there between the longest and shortest route from Fresno to Los Angeles?

   _____

5. The Regan family drove from San Francisco to Palm Springs. They drove 367 miles more than the Levins, who also drove to Palm Springs. What city did the Levins drive from?

   _____

6. Two families drove in different triangle-shaped routes. One family drove 300 miles farther than the other. Which two cities were on both routes?

   _____

Name _____   Date _____

Subtract Greater Numbers

CA Standard
KEY NS 2.1

Find 3,523 − 1,486.

$$\begin{array}{r} {\scriptstyle 11} \\ {\scriptstyle 4\,\cancel{7}\,13} \\ 3,\cancel{5}\cancel{2}\cancel{3} \\ -1,486 \\ \hline 2,037 \end{array}$$

Check:
$$\begin{array}{r} {\scriptstyle 1\,1} \\ 2,037 \\ +1,486 \\ \hline 3,523 \end{array}$$

3,523 − 1,486 = 2,037

Find each difference.

1. $\begin{array}{r} 5,293 \\ -2,716 \\ \hline \end{array}$

2. $\begin{array}{r} 4,200 \\ -3,100 \\ \hline \end{array}$

3. $\begin{array}{r} 7,454 \\ -4,215 \\ \hline \end{array}$

4. $\begin{array}{r} 8,760 \\ -7,386 \\ \hline \end{array}$

5. $\begin{array}{r} 3,549 \\ -2,750 \\ \hline \end{array}$

6. $\begin{array}{r} \$2,177 \\ -\$1,153 \\ \hline \end{array}$

7. $\begin{array}{r} 5,524 \\ -1,603 \\ \hline \end{array}$

8. $\begin{array}{r} 7,243 \\ -4,537 \\ \hline \end{array}$

9. $\begin{array}{r} 1,558 \\ -1,362 \\ \hline \end{array}$

10. $\begin{array}{r} 4,292 \\ -1,728 \\ \hline \end{array}$

11. 6,352 − 3,236 =

12. 2,476 − 1,685 =

13. 5,688 − 3,865 = _____

14. 4,371 − 3,356 = _____

Spiral Review   (Chapter 3, Lesson 2) **KEY AF 1.1**

Find the number or numbers that make the number sentence true.

15. 30 − _____ = 18 + 4

16. 65 + 10 > 72 + _____

17. If Mrs. Cruz was 3 years older, she would be the same age as Mr. Azeroff. Mr. Azeroff is 46 years old. How old is Mrs. Cruz?

_____

Use with text pp. 78–79

Subtract Greater Numbers

CA Standard
KEY NS 2.1

Use the table to solve. Show your work.

1. How many more ships does Japan have than China?

   _____

2. Which country listed in the table has the most ships? Which country has the fewest ships? What is the difference in the number of ships?

   _____

   _____

3. Which country listed in the table has 368 fewer ships than China has?

   _____

4. Andrew says that the United States has 270 more ships than Germany has. What's wrong with Andrew's statement?

   _____

   _____

   _____

| Shipping Fleets Around the World ||
Country	Number of Ships
China	1,974
Germany	1,791
Greece	3,133
Japan	2,712
Norway	1,310
Russia	1,606
United States	1,521

5. Abby says that the United States and Russia have 3,127 ships altogether. How could you use subtraction to check if Abby is correct?

   _____

6. Of all the ships in Greece, 1,345 are dry bulk carriers for shipping grains, sugar, and other loose materials. How many Greek ships are not dry bulk carriers?

   _____

Subtract Across Zeros

CA Standard
KEY NS 2.1

Subtract.

Find 700 − 324.
Regroup from greater places as needed.

$$\begin{array}{r} \overset{9}{6}\overset{}{\cancel{1}}0\,10 \\ 7\cancel{0}\cancel{0} \\ -324 \\ \hline 376 \end{array} \quad \text{Check} \quad \begin{array}{r} \overset{11}{} \\ 376 \\ +324 \\ \hline 700 \end{array}$$

---

1. $\begin{array}{r} 406 \\ -157 \\ \hline \end{array}$ 2. $\begin{array}{r} 905 \\ -453 \\ \hline \end{array}$

3. $\begin{array}{r} 600 \\ -353 \\ \hline \end{array}$ 4. $\begin{array}{r} 803 \\ -626 \\ \hline \end{array}$

5. $\begin{array}{r} 7,009 \\ -3,974 \\ \hline \end{array}$ 6. $\begin{array}{r} 703 \\ -214 \\ \hline \end{array}$ 7. $\begin{array}{r} 306 \\ -148 \\ \hline \end{array}$ 8. $\begin{array}{r} 500 \\ -337 \\ \hline \end{array}$

9. $\begin{array}{r} 800 \\ -246 \\ \hline \end{array}$ 10. $\begin{array}{r} 3,060 \\ -1,436 \\ \hline \end{array}$

11. $470 - 202 =$ 12. $207 - 173 =$

_____   _____

13. $800 - 438 =$ 14. $5,520 - 2,359 =$

_____   _____

Spiral Review   (Chapter 3, Lesson 3) **KEY** NS 2.1, AF 1.0

Find the number that makes the number sentence true. Tell which property you used.

15. $9 + \rule{2cm}{0.4pt} = 9$ 16. $(1 + 6) + 5 = \rule{2cm}{0.4pt} + (6 + 5)$

_____   _____

17. Joey had 8 stickers, Anoush had 4 stickers, and Maria had 10 stickers. Joey gave Maria 2 stickers and Anoush gave Joey 3 stickers. How many stickers did they have in total?

_____

Subtract Across Zeros

Solve.

1. A truck driver drove a total of 904 miles in two days. The first day he drove 456 miles. How many miles did he drive the second day?

   _____

2. The distance between two cable towers on an aerial tramway is 3,000 feet. When a cable car has started at one of the towers and traveled 1,225 feet, how many feet remain before it reaches the other tower?

   _____

3. Maria has 56 ants in a collection. She wants a complete collection of 1,000 ants. How many more ants does she need?

   _____

4. Mr. Diego is driving from Denver, Colorado, to Memphis, Tennessee, this weekend. The total distance is 1,040 miles. If he drives 650 miles on Saturday, how many miles will he have to drive on Sunday?

   _____

5. Air Force One can carry a total of 102 people. The plane always has a crew of 26 people. How many passengers can fly on Air Force One at the same time?

   _____

6. A number made up of the digits 4, 5, and 6 is subtracted from a number made up of the digits 0, 2, 8. The difference is 157. Write out the entire problem.

   _____

Estimate Sums and Differences

CA Standards
NS 1.4, **KEY** NS 2.1

Estimate 88 − 71.

88	rounds to	90
−71	rounds to	−70
		20

88 − 71 is about 20.

Estimate the sum or difference by rounding each number to the greatest place.

1. $\begin{array}{r} 72 \\ +27 \end{array}$ 2. $\begin{array}{r} 94 \\ -13 \end{array}$ 3. $\begin{array}{r} 69 \\ -29 \end{array}$ 4. $\begin{array}{r} 84 \\ -78 \end{array}$

5. $\begin{array}{r} 51 \\ +36 \end{array}$ 6. $\begin{array}{r} 92 \\ -43 \end{array}$ 7. $\begin{array}{r} 370 \\ +114 \end{array}$ 8. $\begin{array}{r} 563 \\ +175 \end{array}$

9. $\begin{array}{r} 776 \\ -171 \end{array}$ 10. $\begin{array}{r} 657 \\ -438 \end{array}$ 11. $78 - 26 =$ 12. $94 - 22 =$

13. $198 - 196 =$ 14. $\$375 + \$119 =$

Spiral Review (Chapter 3, Lessons 4 and 5) **KEY NS 2.1, AF 1.0, MR 2.2**

Add.

15. $\begin{array}{r} 332 \\ 65 \\ +196 \end{array}$ 16. $\begin{array}{r} 5,627 \\ +2,443 \end{array}$

17. A cruise ship had 2,184 passengers and a crew of 695. How many people were on the cruise ship altogether?

_____

Estimate Sums and Differences

CA Standards
NS 1.4, **KEY** NS 2.1

Use estimation to solve each problem.

1. The Wright brothers built and flew the first successful airplane in 1903. On December 17, 1903, their first flight lasted 12 seconds. Their longest flight on that day was 47 seconds longer than their first flight. About how long was their longest flight?

_____

2. The first flight of the Wright Brothers covered a distance of 120 feet. The longest flight on that day was 852 feet. About how much further was the longest flight than the first flight?

_____

3. The Wright brothers' airplane was named *Flyer*. It was 253 inches long. It had a wingspan, or width, of 484 inches. About how much wider was the *Flyer* than it was long?

_____

4. In 1927, Charles Lindbergh flew the first solo non-stop flight across the Atlantic Ocean. Alcock and Brown accomplished the first non-stop flight across the Atlantic in 1919; Lindbergh was the first to solo. His plane, the *Spirit of St. Louis,* had a wingspan that was 68 inches wider than the *Flyer*. About how wide was the *Spirit of St. Louis*?

_____

5. **Reasoning** The *Spirit of St. Louis* weighed 2,150 pounds. The *Flyer* weighed 1,545 pounds less than the *Spirit*. Explain why rounding these two numbers to the greatest place will not give a reasonable estimate for how much the *Flyer* weighed.

_____

_____

_____

6. Laura counted 1487 books on a library shelf. Together three shelves can hold 4,530 books. About how many books can fit on the other two shelves?

_____

Problem Solving: Estimate or Exact Amount?

CA Standards
MR 2.5, MR 2.4

Lea is reading a book that is 128 pages long. She has read 63 pages. About how many more pages does she have left to read?

Step 1 Since the question asks "about how many pages," you can estimate.

Step 2 Round the two numbers to the nearest tens and subtract.

128 ⟶ round to 130   63 ⟶ round to 60

130 − 60 = 70

Solution: Lea has about 70 more pages to read.

Solve. Did you use an estimate or an exact answer?

1. People donated 124 books to the library last month and 139 books this month. How many books were donated in this period? _____

2. The library has 387 DVDs in its collection. A total of 154 DVDs are currently on loan to patrons. To the nearest hundred, how many DVDs are left in the library?

_____

3. Doug owes 75¢ for one overdue library book and $1.10 for another. How much does he owe the library? _____

Spiral Review (Chapter 3, Lesson 4) **KEY NS 2.1, MR 2.2**

Add. Check by adding in a different order.

4.　　51
　　　18
　　+ 21
　　_____

5.　　112
　　　43
　　+ 65
　　_____

6. In April, 132 people camped in Wildwood State Forest. In May, 247 people camped there. In June, 309 people camped in Wildwood. In this 3-month period, how many campers stayed in the state forest?

_____

Name _____ Date _____

Estimate or Exact Amount?

CA Standards
MR 2.5, MR 2.4

Solve each problem. Tell whether you used an estimate or found an exact answer.

1. Mr. Ricco bought a new lawn mower for $220. It came with a mail-in rebate for $35, which he sent in and got back money. What did the lawn mower actually end up costing him?

_____

2. Victor mowed his lawn, which was 1,520 square feet. Then he mowed his neighbor's 1,284-square-foot lawn. To the nearest hundred, how much lawn did Victor mow altogether?

_____

3. Mr. Sanchez took his wife and two children to the circus. Tickets were $7.50 for adults and $5.25 for children. Mr. Sanchez had $30 to spend. Was that enough to pay for the tickets? What, if any, change did he get back?

_____

4. There are 132 people who work in the circus. There are 25 laborers, 6 drivers, and 7 animal keepers. The rest are performers. To the nearest ten, how many circus performers are there?

_____

5. Judy drives 25 miles each way to work and back home. Jorge's commute is 45 miles each way. How many more miles does Jorge drive each week Monday through Friday than Judy does?

_____

6. Middletown to Star City is 232 miles. Middletown to Rileyville is 136 miles in the same direction. About how far is it from Rileyville to Star City to the nearest hundred? How much difference is there between your estimate and the exact number of miles?

_____

Name _____ Date _____

Hands On: Model Multiplication

CA Standards
MR 2.3, **KEY** AF 1.1

Model each set with counters or dots. Then write an addition sentence and a multiplication sentence for each.

Example 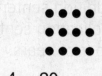	**1.** 2 groups of 7
5 groups of 4	_____
	_____
Solution:	**2.** 6 groups of 5
$4 + 4 + 4 + 4 + 4 = 20$	_____
$5 \times 4 = 20$	_____

3. 7 groups of 3

_____

_____

4. 4 groups of 6

_____

_____

Write a multiplication sentence for each.

5. $6 + 6 + 6 + 6 = 24$

_____

6. $3 + 3 + 3 + 3 + 3 = 15$

_____

7. $2 + 2 + 2 + 2 + 2 = 10$

_____

8. $4 + 4 + 4 = 12$

_____

Spiral Review (Chapter 4, Lessons 2–4) **KEY** NS 2.1

9.
$$\begin{array}{r} 591 \\ -347 \\ \hline \end{array}$$

10.
$$\begin{array}{r} 427 \\ -336 \\ \hline \end{array}$$

11. Julio buys 325 glow-in-the-dark stickers. He gives 59 of them to his younger brother. How many stickers does he have left?

_____

Use with text pp. 100–101

Model Multiplication

Solve each problem.

1. Fill in the blanks to describe the dolls in the collection shown below.

_____ groups of _____ dolls

2. Sally has 4 brown bears, 4 black bears, and 4 gray bears in her stuffed bear collection. Write an addition sentence and a multiplication sentence for the total number of bears.

_____

_____

3. Tony buys 8 identical packs of comic books for his collection. What must you know before you can multiply to find the total number of comic books Tony bought?

_____

_____

4. Jessica has 4 groups of 4 rocks in her rock collection. She says she has 8 rocks altogether. What's wrong?

_____

_____

5. Ben has 5 bags of 6 jellybeans each and 4 bags of 8 jellybeans each. Which group of bags has more jellybeans? How many more?

_____

_____

6. There are 5 groups of 3 students and 3 groups of 4 students in Ms. Hardy's class. If 6 students leave the class, how many students are left?

_____

_____

Name _____ Date _____

Arrays and the Commutative Property

CA Standards
AF 1.5, AF 2.2

Write a multiplication sentence for each array.

Example		Solution:
	2 rows × 3 in each row = 6	2 × **3** = 6
	3 rows × 2 in each row = 6	3 × **2** = 6

1.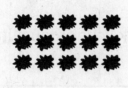

2.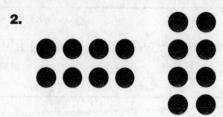

_____

_____

Find each missing number.

3. 8 × 4 = 32

   4 × ___ = 32

4. 9 × 2 = 18

   ___ × 9 = 18

5. 10 × 2 = 20

   2 × 10 = ___

6. 24 = 6 × 4

   24 = 4 × ___

7. 5 × 6 = 30

   6 × ___ = 30

8. 9 × 4 = 36

   4 × 9 = ___

9. 7 × 9 = 63

   ___ × 7 = 63

10. 72 = 8 × 9

    72 = 9 × ___

Spiral Review (Chapter 3, Lesson 2) **KEY** AF 1.1

Write <, > or = for each .

11. 5,483  5,932

12. 429 410

13. Janie has 1,244 pennies and Margot has 1,459 pennies. Who has more pennies?

_____

Arrays and the Commutative Property

CA Standards
AF 1.5, AF 2.2

Solve.

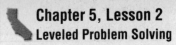

1. Fill in the blanks to describe the sheet of stickers.

   _____ rows of _____ stickers

2. Multiply to find the total number of stickers that are on the sheet.

   _____

3. **Reasoning** How can you use addition to check your product in Problem 2?

   _____

4. Marcos buys a sheet of stickers that has 3 rows of stickers. Each row has the same number of stickers. After he takes one of the stickers off, there are 20 stickers left on the sheet. How many stickers were in each row of the sheet Marcos bought? Explain how you know.

   _____

   _____

5. **Reasoning** A checkerboard has 8 rows of 8 squares. Half of the squares are black. How many squares on the checkerboard are black? Explain.

   _____

6. Mary wants to put all of her stamps on a single page. She has one page with 3 rows of 8 stamps, another page with 4 rows of 5 stamps, and a third page with 6 rows of 4 stamps. Her new single page has 7 rows and can fit 10 stamps across. Can she fit all her stamps on the new page? Explain.

   _____

   _____

Multiplication Review: 2, 5, and 10

CA Standards
KEY NS 2.2, KEY AF 1.1

Find the product 3 × 2.

Way 1 There are 3
groups of 2.
$3 \times 2 = 6$

Way 2 Skip count:
2, 4, 6.

Way 3 Use repeated
addition.
$2 + 2 + 2 = 6$

Solution: $3 \times 2 = 6$

Find the product.

1. 2
×2

2. 2
×4

3. 7
×2

4. 2
×9

5. 8
×2

6. 3
×2

7. 5
×3

8. 7
×5

9. 5
×8

10. 9
×5

11. 5
×1

12. 2
×5

13. 10
×3

14. 7
×10

15. 10
×8

16. 9
×10

17. 10
×1

18. 10
×2

Spiral Review (Chapter 3, Lesson 2) **KEY AF 1.1**

Write <, > or = for each ⬭.

19. 23 + 45 ⬭ 95

20. 55 – 42 ⬭ 13

21. Randy has one box of 12 cookies and another box of 34 cookies. Jamal has one box of 48 cookies. Use <, >, or = to compare the number of cookies Jamal and Randy have.

Multiplication Review: 2, 5, and 10

Use the table to solve each problem.

Party Favors Package	
Party Favor	**Number in Each Package**
Beach Balls	2
Balloons	9
Trading Cards	6
Stickers	8
Kazoos	5
Tattoos	7
Noise Makers	3
Bubble Makers	4

1. Tanya buys five packages of balloons for her birthday party. How many balloons does she buy in all?

_____

2. Karl buys 10 packages of noise makers for a party. How many noise makers does he buy all together?

_____

3. **Reasoning** Felicia buys two packages of a party favor. She now has 12 of those items in all. Which party favor did Felicia buy?

_____

4. Vince used two packages of kazoos to make party favor bags for his party. He put one kazoo in each bag and gave one bag to each guest. How many guests came to Vince's party?

_____

5. A package of tattoos costs $3. A package of stickers costs $4. Steve buys two packages of each. How much money does he spend in all?

_____

6. Larry says that one package of balloons has twice as many party favors as one package of bubble makers. What's wrong?

_____

_____

Multiply with 4

Write a multiplication sentence for each picture.

Example

There are 5 groups of 4 each.

5 groups × 4 in each group = 20

Solution: $5 \times 4 = 20$

1.

2.

3.

_____ _____ _____

Multiply.

4.	5.	6.	7.	8.	9.
1 ×4	4 ×4	4 ×7	8 ×4	4 ×5	2 ×4

Find each missing number.

10. $7 \times 4 = 28$

$4 \times \_\_\_ = 28$

11. $36 = 9 \times 4$

$36 = 4 \times \_\_\_$

12. $4 \times 3 = 12$

$3 \times 4 = \_\_\_$

Spiral Review (Chapter 4, Lesson 2) **KEY** NS 2.1

Substract. Check using addition.

13.
$$\begin{array}{r} 432 \\ -215 \\ \hline \end{array}$$

14.
$$\begin{array}{r} 638 \\ -514 \\ \hline \end{array}$$

15. Marlena has 244 stamps in her stamp collection. If she gives 36 stamps to her brother, how many does she have left?

_____

Name _____ Date _____

Multiply with 4

CA Standards
KEY NS 2.2, MR 2.3

Yang collects stamps from countries in South America. He made the pictograph below to show his collection. Use the pictograph to solve each problem.

1. How many stamps does Yang have from Argentina?

_____

2. How many stamps in Yang's collection are from Venezuela?

_____

3. From which country does Yang have the most stamps? How many of those stamps does he have?

Yang's Stamp Collection	
Country	**Number of Stamps**
Argentina	🖼🖼🖼🖼🖼🖼
Bolivia	🖼🖼🖼
Brazil	🖼🖼🖼🖼🖼🖼🖼🖼🖼
Chile	🖼🖼🖼🖼🖼🖼🖼🖼
Colombia	🖼🖼🖼🖼
Ecuador	🖼🖼
Peru	🖼🖼🖼🖼
Venezuela	🖼🖼🖼🖼🖼🖼🖼

Each 🖼 stands for 4 stamps.

_____

4. Yang's sister Hyun looks at his pictograph and says that Yang has 8 stamps from Chile in his collection. What mistake did Hyun make?

_____

_____

5. Yang wants to take his stamps from Brazil and Venezuela and put them on a separate page. How many stamps will be on the page?

_____

6. If Yang gives 16 Brazil stamps to his sister Hyun, how many more Venezuela stamps than Brazil stamps will he have?

_____

Hands On: Multiply with 0 and 1

Property of One	Zero Property
The product of any number and 1 is that number.	The product of any number and 0 is 0.
$1 \times 8 = 8$ $8 \times 1 = 8$	$9 \times 0 = 0$ $0 \times 9 = 0$

Multiply.

1. $\begin{array}{r} 9 \\ \times 1 \\ \hline \end{array}$
2. $\begin{array}{r} 4 \\ \times 0 \\ \hline \end{array}$
3. $\begin{array}{r} 6 \\ \times 1 \\ \hline \end{array}$
4. $\begin{array}{r} 1 \\ \times 7 \\ \hline \end{array}$
5. $\begin{array}{r} 10 \\ \times 0 \\ \hline \end{array}$

6. $\begin{array}{r} 3 \\ \times 0 \\ \hline \end{array}$
7. $\begin{array}{r} 1 \\ \times 3 \\ \hline \end{array}$
8. $\begin{array}{r} 5 \\ \times 1 \\ \hline \end{array}$
9. $\begin{array}{r} 0 \\ \times 3 \\ \hline \end{array}$
10. $\begin{array}{r} 8 \\ \times 1 \\ \hline \end{array}$

11. 10×1 _____
12. 2×1 _____
13. 6×1 _____
14. 0×6 _____

Spiral Review (Chapter 5, Lesson 3) **KEY** NS 2.2

15. $\begin{array}{r} 4 \\ \times 10 \\ \hline \end{array}$
16. $\begin{array}{r} 8 \\ \times 5 \\ \hline \end{array}$

17. Jon has 4 fishbowls. There are 5 fish in each bowl. How many fish does Jon have in all? _____

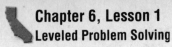
Hands On: Multiply with 0 and 1

CA Standards
NS 2.6, MR 3.3

Solve each problem.

1. Peter threw a basketball 12 times. It missed the basket every time. Write a multiplication sentence to show Peter's score.

_____

_____

2. Ari threw a basketball 6 times. It went into the basket every time. Write a multiplication sentence to show Ari's score. (Each basket = 1 point.)

_____

_____

3. Andrea's dog Banjo buried 1 bone in the yard every day for one week. Write a multiplication sentence to show how many bones Banjo buried in all.

_____

_____

4. Banjo forgot where he buried his bones! He dug 1 hole every day for two weeks, but he didn't find any bones. Write a multiplication sentence to show how many bones Banjo found.

_____

_____

5. Vivian gave a pizza party and invited 31 friends. She put 1 slice of pizza on each plate. Write a multiplication sentence to show how many slices of pizza in all were on the plates.

_____

_____

6. After everyone ate pizza, how many slices in all were left on the plates? Write a multiplication sentence.

_____

_____

Multiply with 9

**CA Standards
KEY NS 2.2, AF 1.2**

$9 \times 9 = \square$

You can use patterns to find 9s facts.

Think: The tens digit will be 1 less than the factor you are multiplying by 9.

$9 - 1 = 8$

Solution: $9 \times 9 = 81$

Think: The sum of the digits in the product will be 9.

$8 + 1 = 9$

Multiply.

1. $\begin{array}{r} 9 \\ \times 3 \\ \hline \end{array}$
2. $\begin{array}{r} 1 \\ \times 9 \\ \hline \end{array}$
3. $\begin{array}{r} 8 \\ \times 9 \\ \hline \end{array}$
4. $\begin{array}{r} 9 \\ \times 9 \\ \hline \end{array}$

5. $\begin{array}{r} 9 \\ \times 4 \\ \hline \end{array}$
6. $\begin{array}{r} 6 \\ \times 9 \\ \hline \end{array}$
7. $\begin{array}{r} 7 \\ \times 9 \\ \hline \end{array}$
8. $\begin{array}{r} 9 \\ \times 0 \\ \hline \end{array}$

9. $9 \times 5 = $ _____
10. $2 \times 9 = $ _____
11. $10 \times 9 = $ _____

Spiral Review (Chapter 5, Lesson 4) **KEY NS 2.2**

12. $\begin{array}{r} 4 \\ \times 8 \\ \hline \end{array}$
13. $\begin{array}{r} 7 \\ \times 4 \\ \hline \end{array}$

14. Suki worked on math problems for 2 hours on Monday, 2 hours on Tuesday, 2 hours on Wednesday, 2 hours on Thursday, and 2 hours on Friday. How many hours did she study math in all?

_____

Name _____ Date _____

Multiply with 9

CA Standards
KEY NS 2.2, AF 1.2

Solve each problem about foods from rain forests.

1. Cashews, Brazil nuts, and peanuts originally grew in rain forests. Anne made a trail mix with 9 cups of each. How many cups of cashews, Brazil nuts, and peanuts did she use in all?

   _____

2. Yams also grow in rain forests. Connie cooked 9 yams for Thanksgiving dinner. Her friend Crystal cooked twice as many yams. How many yams did Crystal cook?

   _____

3. Barney loves pineapple. He eats 1 slice at breakfast every day. He cuts the pineapple into 7 slices for the week. How many slices does Barney eat in 9 weeks?

   _____

4. Vanilla comes from the seeds of rain forest orchids. The seeds grow in long, thin pods. Nine workers each pick 5 orchids in the morning. They each pick 8 orchids in the afternoon. How many orchids do they pick in all?

   _____

5. Rain forests give us oranges. One slice of an orange contains 9 milligrams vitamin C. Doctors recommend that children consume 45 milligrams of vitamin C each day. How many orange slices should you eat to get the vitamin C you need each day?

   _____

6. Chocolate comes from the rain forest cocoa plant. One ounce of milk chocolate contains 9 grams of fat. How many grams of fat from cocoa are in ten 6-ounce milk chocolate bars?

   _____

Square Arrays

CA Standards
KEY NS 2.2, MR 2.3

You can use a square array to multiply.

$4 \times 4 = \square$

Model it:

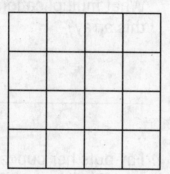

Count:

1	2	3	4
5	6	7	8
9	10	11	12
13	14	15	16

Solution: $4 \times 4 = 16$

Draw an array to find the product. Use grid paper.

1. $2 \times 2 =$ _____

2. $3 \times 3 =$ _____

3. $5 \times 5 =$ _____

4. $6 \times 6 =$ _____

5. $7 \times 7 =$ _____

6. $8 \times 8 =$ _____

7. $9 \times 9 =$ _____

8. $10 \times 10 =$ _____

Spiral Review (Chapter 4, Lesson 5) NS 1.4, **KEY** NS 2.1

9. Estimate the sum by rounding each number to the greatest place.

$$\begin{array}{r} 563 \\ +312 \\ \hline \end{array}$$

10. Estimate the difference by rounding each number to the greatest place.

$$\begin{array}{r} 836 \\ -481 \\ \hline \end{array}$$

11. Flora traveled 795 miles from Dallas to Atlanta. Then she traveled 841 miles from Atlanta to New York. About how many miles did Flora travel in all?

_____

Square Arrays

CA Standards
KEY NS 2.2, MR 2.3

Solve each problem.

1. Cam's bookcase has 8 shelves. There are 8 books on each shelf. How many books does Cam have in the bookcase?

_____

2. A square box holds 49 tennis balls. What multiplication fact goes with this array?

_____

3. Fay bakes 32 cupcakes. She puts them in a box that has 5 rows, with 5 cupcakes in each row. How many cupcakes do **not** fit in the box?

_____

4. Fay puts her cupcakes in a larger box. This box has 6 rows, with 6 cupcakes in each row. How many empty spaces are in the box?

_____

5. Ralph assembles his toy dinosaurs into a square array. He tries a 6 × 6 array, but it is too small. Then, he tries an 8 × 8 array, but it is too big. How many dinosaurs do you think Ralph has?

_____

6. Inés collects shells. She displays them in 2 boxes. One box has 9 rows, with 9 shells in each row. The other box has 10 rows, with 10 shells in each row. How many shells does Inés have in all?

_____

Homework and Problem Solving
54
Use with text pp. 128–130

Multiply with 3

CA Standard
KEY NS 2.2

You can use different ways to find 6×3.

Skip count by 3s.	Make equal groups.	Draw an array.
Say: 3, 6, 9, 12, 15, 18	Draw a picture. Then use repeated addition.	6 rows of 3 is 18.
Solution: $6 \times 3 = 18$	$3+3+3+3+3+3 = 18$	

Find the product.

1. $\begin{array}{r} 3 \\ \times\ 6 \\ \hline \end{array}$
2. $\begin{array}{r} 3 \\ \times\ 4 \\ \hline \end{array}$
3. $\begin{array}{r} 9 \\ \times\ 3 \\ \hline \end{array}$
4. $\begin{array}{r} 3 \\ \times\ 5 \\ \hline \end{array}$
5. $\begin{array}{r} 3 \\ \times\ 3 \\ \hline \end{array}$

6. $7 \times 3 =$ _____

7. $3 \times 8 =$ _____

8. $3 \times 5 =$ _____

9. $3 \times 10 =$ _____

10. $1 \times 3 =$ _____

11. $3 \times 2 =$ _____

Spiral Review (Chapter 5, Lesson 2 – 4) **AF 1.5, AF 2.2**

12. $\begin{array}{r} 9 \\ \times\ 5 \\ \hline \end{array}$

13. $\begin{array}{r} 4 \\ \times\ 9 \\ \hline \end{array}$

14. A store has 3 rows of T-shirts, with 8 shirts in each row. How many T-shirts are there in all? _____

Multiply with 3

CA Standard
KEY NS 2.2

Solve each problem.

1. Both of my factors are the same number. My product is 9. What are my two factors?

   _____

2. There are 3 groups of hikers in the Rain Forest Hiking Club. There are 7 hikers in each group. Draw arrows on the number line below to skip count by 3s to find the total number of hikers in the club.

   _____

3. A Xenops (ZEN-ops) is a rain forest bird. There are 18 Xenops eggs. How many groups of 3 eggs are there?

   _____

4. Crocodiles live in rain forests. One crocodile lays 3×5 eggs. A second crocodile lays 24 eggs. How many more eggs does the second crocodile lay?

   _____

5. In May, the hiking club members hiked 3 miles each weekend. In June, they hiked 6 miles each weekend. In July, they hiked 12 miles each weekend. If this pattern continues, how many miles are the club members likely to hike each weekend in August?

6. Many kinds of lizards live in rain forests. One lizard eats $(3 \times 3) + (3 \times 3) + (3 \times 3)$ insects. Another lizard eats $(3 \times 5) + (3 \times 5)$ insects. Which lizard eats more insects? How many more?

Problem Solving: Multistep Problems

Solve each multistep problem.

Henry has 8 model trucks. He has three times as many model cars. How many model trucks and model cars does Henry have in all?

Step ❶ First, find the number of model cars Henry has. Remember, he has 3 times as many model cars as model trucks.

$8 \times 3 = 24$ model cars

Step ❷ Next, add the number of model cars to the number of model trucks to find the total.

$24 + 8 = 32$

Solution: Henry has 32 model trucks and model cars in all.

---

1. Frank receives from his parents $3 each week for washing the dishes and $2 each week for vacuuming. How much money does Frank receive from his parents in 6 weeks?

   _____

2. Bonnie has 4 nonfiction books. She has four times as many fiction books. How many more fiction books does Bonnie have than nonfiction books?

   _____

3. Samantha collected 5 seashells. Ryan collected three times as many seashells. How many seashells did Samantha and Ryan collect in all?

   _____

Spiral Review (Chapter 5, Lesson 2) **AF 1.5, AF 2.2**

Find each missing number.

4. $24 = 8 \times 3$

   $24 = 3 \times$ ____

5. $30 = 6 \times 5$

   ____ $= 5 \times 6$

6. Ellen has filled a page of her stamp album with 6 rows of 6 stamps each. How many stamps are on this page of Ellen's stamp album?

   _____

Name _____ Date _____

Problem Solving: Multistep Problems

CA Standards
MR 1.2, NS 2.8

Contrary to their name, most anteaters eat insects other than just ants. There are 3 main kinds of anteaters and most of them live in the South and Central American rain forests. Solve each problem about anteaters and their relatives.

1. The smallest anteater is the silky anteater. It is 1 foot long. The largest anteater is the giant anteater. It is 6 times as long as the silky anteater. What is the difference in these two anteaters' lengths?

2. The giant anteater's tail is $\frac{1}{2}$ foot less than half its total length. How long is its tail?

3. The collared anteater is 4 times as long as the silky anteater. Its tail is half its length. How long is the collared anteater's tail?

4. The giant armadillo is a relative of the anteater. It weighs about 15 pounds. The giant anteater weighs 5 times as much. What is the combined weight of the giant armadillo and the giant anteater?

5. The sloth is another relative of the anteater. It also lives in South and Central America, but eats mostly plants. The sloth grows to a length of about 24 inches. There are 2.5 centimeters in an inch and 12 inches in a foot. How many feet long is a sloth?

6. The aardvark is not related to the anteater, but it also lives on a diet of ants and termites. The aardvark weighs as much as 2 giant anteaters, minus 10 pounds. How much does an aardvark weigh?

Hands On: Use a Multiplication Table

What pattern do you see in the column for 3?

Look at the column for 3. What numbers do you see?

0, 3, 6, 9, 12, 15, 18, 21, 24, 27, and 30

The number increases by 3 each time.

The pattern in the column for 3 is add 3, or skip count by 3.

×	0	1	2	3	4	5	6	7	8	9	10
0	0	0	0	0	0	0	0	0	0	0	0
1	0	1	2	3	4	5	6	7	8	9	10
2	0	2	4	6	8	10	12	14	16	18	20
3	0	3	6	9	12	15	18	21	24	27	30
4	0	4	8	12	16	20	24	28	32	36	40
5	0	5	10	15	20	25	30	35	40	45	50
6	0	6	12	18	24	30	36	42	48	54	60
7	0	7	14	21	28	35	42	49	56	63	70
8	0	8	16	24	32	40	48	56	64	72	80
9	0	9	18	27	36	45	54	63	72	81	90
10	0	10	20	30	40	50	60	70	80	90	100

Use the multiplication table to answer each question.

1. What do all the products in the column for 5 have in common?

_____

_____

2. Which rows and columns have products that are all odd numbers?

_____

_____

Spiral Review   (Chapter 5, Lesson 3) **KEY** NS 2.2, **KEY** AF 1.1

3. Multiply.

$$\begin{array}{r} 5 \\ \times\, 9 \\ \hline \end{array}$$

4. Multiply.

$$\begin{array}{r} 5 \\ \times\, 7 \\ \hline \end{array}$$

5. Josh has 6 blank pages left in his sticker book. He wants to put 5 stickers on each blank page. How many stickers does he need? _____

Hands On: Use a Multiplication Table

CA Standard
KEY NS 2.2

Solve each problem.

1. At the Florida Aquarium in Tampa, 9 eels each had 5 babies. How many baby eels are there in all?

   _____

2. At the Virginia State Fair in Richmond, Millie sold apples. She sold 10 bags with 4 apples in each bag. How many apples did Millie sell in all?

   _____

3. At the San Francisco Zoo, 3 gorillas ate 5 bananas each, and 4 chimpanzees ate 2 bananas each. How many bananas did they eat in all?

   _____

4. On Tuesday, six children spent 3 hours each at the science museum in Philadelphia. Four children spent 2 hours each at the museum on Wednesday. How many hours did the children spend there in all?

   _____

5. The Freedom Trail in Boston is 3 miles long. Seven people walked the trail on Saturday. Eight people walked the trail on Sunday. One person walked the trail on Monday. How many *miles* did they walk in all?

   _____

6. At the Flower Show in Atlanta, Georgia, 7 people each bought 7 roses, 6 people each bought 6 tulips, and 5 people each bought 5 lilies. How many flowers did they buy in all?

   _____

Multiply with 6, 7, and 8

CA Standards
KEY NS 2.2, AF 1.5

$6 \times 5 = \square$

You can use doubling

6×5 is double 3×5.

$3 \times 5 = 15$

$15 + 15 = 30$

Solution: $6 \times 5 = 30$

3×5 3×5

6×5

Multiply.

1. $\begin{array}{r} 6 \\ \times 3 \\ \hline \end{array}$

2. $\begin{array}{r} 6 \\ \times 6 \\ \hline \end{array}$

3. $\begin{array}{r} 10 \\ \times 6 \\ \hline \end{array}$

4. $\begin{array}{r} 8 \\ \times 6 \\ \hline \end{array}$

5. $\begin{array}{r} 5 \\ \times 6 \\ \hline \end{array}$

6. $\begin{array}{r} 7 \\ \times 6 \\ \hline \end{array}$

7. $6 \times 8 = $ _____

8. $7 \times 8 = $ _____

9. $7 \times 7 = $ _____

10. $8 \times 7 = $ _____

11. $4 \times 6 = $ _____

12. $6 \times 7 = $ _____

Spiral Review   (Chapter 4, Lessons 2–4) **KEY** NS 2.1

13. Subtract.

$\begin{array}{r} 726 \\ -458 \\ \hline \end{array}$

14. Subtract.

$\begin{array}{r} 5,314 \\ -1,623 \\ \hline \end{array}$

15. In April, 935 people went to the top of the Sears Tower in Chicago. In May, 1,027 people went to the top. How many more people went to the top of the tower in May than in April?

_____

Multiply with 6, 7, and 8

CA Standards
KEY NS 2.2, AF 1.5

Solve each problem.

1. A touchdown in football is worth 6 points. How many points are 9 touchdowns worth?

_____

2. Dante walks 4 blocks to school and 4 blocks home. How many blocks does he walk in 3 days to and from school?

_____

3. There are 5 ounces of trail mix in a bag. Joan made 5 bags of trail mix. Then she made 3 more bags. How many *ounces* of trail mix did she make in all?

_____

4. Jake's cat naps 4 hours every afternoon. How many hours in all does the cat nap in 2 weeks?

_____

5. In 1958, there were 48 states in the United States. There were 6 rows of stars on the U.S. flag. How many stars were in each row?

_____

6. In 1959, there were 49 states in the United States. There were 7 rows of stars on the U.S. flag. How many stars were in each row?

_____

Practice Multiplying with 6, 7, and 8

CA Standards
KEY NS 2.2, AF 1.5

$3 \times 7 = \square$

You can use a fact you know.

Remember that numbers can be multiplied in any order.

You know that $7 \times 3 = 21$, so $3 \times 7 = 21$.

Solution: $3 \times 7 = 21$

Find the product.

1. $\begin{array}{r} 6 \\ \times 7 \\ \hline \end{array}$
2. $\begin{array}{r} 7 \\ \times 8 \\ \hline \end{array}$
3. $\begin{array}{r} 10 \\ \times 7 \\ \hline \end{array}$

4. $\begin{array}{r} 7 \\ \times 4 \\ \hline \end{array}$
5. $\begin{array}{r} 7 \\ \times 5 \\ \hline \end{array}$
6. $\begin{array}{r} 7 \\ \times 7 \\ \hline \end{array}$

7. $5 \times 7 = $ _____
8. $7 \times 7 = $ _____
9. $8 \times 6 = $ _____

10. $8 \times 5 = $ _____
11. $7 \times 6 = $ _____
12. $7 \times 9 = $ _____

Spiral Review (Chapter 5, Lessons 2–4) **AF 1.5, KEY AF 1.1, AF 2.2, KEY NS 2.2**

13. Multiply.

$\begin{array}{r} 5 \\ \times 6 \\ \hline \end{array}$

14. Multiply.

$\begin{array}{r} 9 \\ \times 4 \\ \hline \end{array}$

15. Tommy has 16 toy trucks. How many different arrays can he make with all the trucks? What are the arrays?

Practice Multiplying by 6, 7, and 8

CA Standards
KEY NS 2.2, AF 1.5

Solve each problem about an interesting plant you can see at many botanical gardens around the United States (*botanical* means "plants").

1. The Venus flytrap is a plant that eats live flies, other insects, and spiders! A Venus flytrap eats 3 insects a month. How many insects does it eat in 8 months?

2. Most Venus flytraps have 7 leaves. How many leaves do 6 flytraps have?

3. The San Francisco Botanical Garden has 7 Venus flytraps. The Brooklyn Botanic Garden has triple that amount. How many flytraps does the Brooklyn garden have?

4. The Berkeley Botanical Garden has 6 Venus flytraps that eat 2 insects a month and 9 flytraps that eat 3 insects a month. How many insects do they eat in all in a month?

5. Altogether, the Venus flytraps at the New York Botanical Garden ate 4×8 insects in one month. The flytraps at the Los Angeles Arboretum (ar-buh-REE-tum; a place where trees and plants are grown) ate 5×7 insects. How many insects did all the flytraps eat?

6. The Venus flytraps at the Santa Barbara Botanical Garden ate 10×4 spiders in May. They ate 5×8 spiders in June. In which month did they eat more? How many more?

Use the Associative Property

CA Standard
AF 1.5

Find the product of $3 \times 2 \times 5$.

Use the Associative Property of Multiplication.

The way factors are grouped does not change the product. (Remember to multiply factors in parentheses first.)

You can multiply
3×2 first.

$(3 \times 2) \times 5 =$
$\qquad 6 \times 5 = 30$

You can multiply
2×5 first.

$3 \times (2 \times 5) =$
$\qquad 3 \times 10 = 30$

No matter which two factors you multiply first, the product will be the same.

Find the product. Multiply factors in parentheses first.

1. $7 \times (3 \times 2) =$ _____

2. $(4 \times 2) \times 3 =$ _____

3. $8 \times (0 \times 3) =$ _____

4. $7 \times (2 \times 2) =$ _____

5. $(5 \times 2) \times 5 =$ _____

6. $(3 \times 3) \times 6 =$ _____

7. $6 \times (3 \times 2) =$ _____

8. $(2 \times 5) \times 7 =$ _____

9. $7 \times (3 \times 1) =$ _____

10. $(4 \times 2) \times 9 =$ _____

Spiral Review (Chapter 6, Lesson 3) **KEY** NS 2.2, MR 2.3

11. Find the product:

$8 \times 8 =$ _____

12. Find the product:

$6 \times 6 =$ _____

13. Martin lined up his baseball caps. He has 7 rows, with 7 caps in each row. How many caps does he have in all?

_____

Use the Associative Property

Solve each problem.

1. Diego bought 7 sheets of stamps. Each sheet had 3 rows of 3 stamps per row. How many stamps did Diego buy in all?

   _____

2. Jim, Angie, and Ryan each drew 2 picture books of their favorite places in San Francisco, California. They drew 5 pictures in each book. How many pictures did they draw in all?

   _____

3. Pairs of students will give oral reports on the cities where they were born. Each student will give a 5-minute report. There are 8 pairs of students. How many *minutes* are needed for all the reports?

   _____

4. Four children have the same birthday. At their party, each child had 1 cake. There were 8 candles on each cake. How many candles were there in all?

   _____

5. There are 5 grown-up pandas and 4 baby pandas at the zoo in Washington, DC. The baby pandas eat 5 pieces of bamboo every day. How many pieces of bamboo do they eat all together in 2 days?

   _____

6. Wendy and her brother Nathan are 8-year-old twins. They each drink 3 glasses of milk every day. How many glasses of milk do they drink all together in 1 week?

   _____

Problem Solving: Guess and Check

Use guess and check to solve each problem.

> Joe is 3 years older than his brother Phillip. Together their ages total 27. How old is each brother?
>
> **Step ❶** Review the facts that you know. Their ages add up to 27. Joe is 3 years older than Phillip.
>
> **Step ❷** Think of 2 numbers that have a difference of 3 and then check to see if they add up to 27.
>
> **Guess**
> 13 − 10 = 3
> 17 − 14 = 3
> 15 − 12 = 3
>
> **Check**
> 13 + 10 = 23 (Guess higher)
> 17 + 14 = 31 (Guess lower)
> 15 + 12 = 27 (Correct)
>
> **Solution:** Joe is 15 and Phillip is 12 years old.

1. Emily and Kaitlin together have 35 stuffed animals. Emily has 7 more stuffed animals than Kaitlin. How many stuffed animals does each girl have?

_____

2. Noah has a total of 45 toy cars and trucks. He has 5 more toy cars than toy trucks. How many toy trucks does he have?

_____

3. Leo has 8 more markers than colored pencils. He has a total of 32 markers and colored pencils. How many of each kind does he have?

_____

Spiral Review (Chapter 5, Lesson 2) **AF 1.5**

Draw an array to find the product. Use grid paper.

4. 3×3

5. 8×8

6. Four groups of 3 students worked on science projects. How many students worked on science projects? _____

Name _____   Date _____

Problem Solving: Guess and Check

CA Standards
MR 2.0, NS 2.0

Use a guess and check strategy to solve each problem.

1. A caterpillar has twice as many legs as a spider. Together, they have 24 legs. How many legs does the spider have? How many legs does the caterpillar have?

_____

2. A male black widow spider is half the size of a female black widow spider. Together, they are 21 millimeters (mm) in length. How big is a female black widow? A male?

_____

3. Two house spiders caught 14 flies in their respective webs over a week's time. The larger spider caught 2 more flies than the smaller spider. How many flies did each spider catch?

_____

4. An average-sized female spider and a large spider can lay a total of 2,100 eggs at one time. The large spider lays 20 times the number of eggs as the average–sized spider. How many eggs does the average-sized spider lay?

_____

5. At the Natural History museum Paula saw 5 times as many beetles as spiders. She saw 6 more spiders than caterpillars. If Paula saw 50 insects and spiders, how many of each kind did she see?

_____

6. In Harry's attic there are three spider webs. The first web is twice as large as the second web. The third web is 3 inches larger than the first web. The combined width of the three webs is 1 foot and 6 inches. How long is each web?

_____

Hands On: Measure to the Nearest Inch

CA Standard
MG 1.1

Estimate.
The battery is about 3 inches long.

Use a ruler.

0   1   2
inches

To the nearest inch, the battery is 2 inches long.

Estimate and then measure each object below to the nearest inch.

1.

Estimate: _____

Measurement: _____

2.

Estimate: _____

Measurement: _____

Use a ruler. Draw a line of each length.

3. 2 inches

4. 3 inches

5. 5 inches

Spiral Review (Chapter 6, Lesson 3) **KEY** NS 2.2, MR 2.3

For 6–7, write whether the array shows a square number. If not, write how many dots should be added to make a square number.

6.

7.

_____   _____

8. Zachary arranged his model cars in an array of 6 rows and 6 columns. How many cars does Zachary have? _____

Hands on: Measure to the Nearest Inch

For Problems 1–3, estimate and then measure each of Keith's school supply objects to the nearest inch. Then use your measurements to solve Problems 4–5.

1.

   _____

2.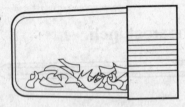

   _____

3.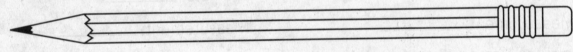

   _____

4. There are 12 inches in 1 foot. Which of the school supply items is closest to $\frac{1}{2}$ foot long?

   _____

5. About how many times longer is the pencil than the pencil sharpener?

   _____

6. Suppose you use the pencil so that it becomes 1 inch shorter. About how much difference will there be between the length of the pencil and the length of the eraser?

   _____

Convert Customary Units of Length

Choose the better estimate for the height of a man.

    a. 6 feet   **b.** 6 miles

A man is much shorter than 1 mile.

The better estimate is 6 feet or choice a.

Customary Units of Length
1 foot = 12 inches
1 yard = 3 feet
1 yard = 36 inches
1 mile = 1,760 yards
1 mile = 5,280 feet

Circle the letter of the better estimate.

1. the height of a tall tree

    a. 50 feet   **b.** 50 inches

2. the height of a skyscraper

    a. 200 miles   **b.** 200 yards

3. the length of a pair of pants

    a. 1 inch   **b.** 1 yard

4. the length of a roll of kite string

    a. 300 yards   **b.** 300 miles

Complete.

5. 3 ft = _____ in.

6. 4 yd = _____ ft

7. 2 yd = _____ in.

8. 24 in. = _____ ft

9. 9 ft = _____ yd

10. 2 ft = _____ in.

Spiral Review (Chapter 4, Lesson 5; Chapter 8, Lesson 2) NS 1.4, **KEY** NS 2.1, MG 1.4

For 11–12, estimate the sum or difference by rounding each number to the greatest place.

11. 721
  +192
  ‾‾‾‾‾

12. 512
  −184
  ‾‾‾‾‾

13. Becky and Ned made banners. Becky's banner is 3 yards long. Ned's banner is 6 feet long. Who made the longer banner?

_____

Name _____ Date _____

Convert Customary Units of Length

Use the table to solve the problems. Show your work.

1. How many feet long is each end zone? What is the combined length, in feet, of the field's two end zones?

_____

2. Give the width of the goal post crossbar using only yards and inches.

_____

3. How many times longer is the field than the end zone?

_____

4. Is the football field 3 feet long, 30 feet long, or 300 feet long? Explain your choice.

_____

_____

_____

5. Tyler says that the football field is wider than it is long. What mistake did he make?

_____

_____

Professional Football Measurements	
Height of Goal Post Crossbar	10 feet
Length of Ball	11 inches
Length of End Zone	10 Yards
Length of Field	100 yards
Width of Field	160 feet
Width of Goal Post Crossbar	$18\frac{1}{2}$ feet

6. Suppose you laid 300 footballs end-to-end beginning at one end of a football field. Would you reach the other end of the field? Explain.

_____

_____

_____

_____

Hands On: Centimeters and Millimeters

CA Standards
MG 1.1, MR 2.5

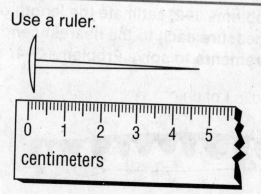

Estimate the length of the nail.

The nail is about 5 centimeters long.

Use a ruler.

To the nearest centimeter, the nail is 5 centimeters long.

To the nearest millimeter, the nail is 47 millimeters.

Estimate in centimeters and then measure each object below to the nearest centimeter and nearest millimeter.

1.

Estimate: _____ cm

Measure to nearest centimeter:

_____ cm

Measure to nearest millimeter:

_____ mm

2.

Estimate: _____ cm

Measure to nearest centimeter:

_____ cm

Measure to nearest millimeter:

_____ mm

Spiral Review   (Chapter 4, Lesson 4) **KEY** NS 2.1

Find the difference.

3.   600
      − 423

4.   1,900
      − 672

5. There are 1,500 seats in the auditorium. If 914 people are sitting in the auditorium, how many seats are left? _____

Name _____ Date _____

Hands On: Centimeters and Millimeters

CA Standards
MG 1.1, MR 2.5

**For Problems 1–2, estimate the length of each tropical fish.
Then measure each to the nearest centimeter. Use your
measurements to solve Problems 3–4.**

1. Coolie Loach

_____

2. Bloodfin

_____

3. Which fish above is closest to
100 millimeters long? Which fish is
closest to 50 millimeters long?

_____

4. A blue gularis is twice as long as
a bloodfin. How long is the blue
gularis in millimeters?

_____

5. A clown loach in a fish tank is 10
centimeters long. In the wild, a
clown loach grows 3 times longer.
Phil says a wild clown loach is 30
centimeters long. Wendy says it is
300 millimeters long. Who is right?
Explain.

_____

_____

_____

6. Greg is measuring the available
space in his room for an aquarium.
Should he measure to the nearest
millimeter or to the nearest
centimeter? Explain.

_____

_____

_____

_____

Convert Metric Units of Length

Meters and **kilometers** are used to measure larger distances than millimeters and centimeters.

Metric Units of Length
1 centimeter = 10 millimeters
1 meter = 100 centimeters
1 kilometer = 1,000 meters

A meter (m) is about the same as a yard.

A kilometer (km) is a little over one half mile.

Choose the unit you would use to measure each. Write *mm, cm, m,* or *km*.

1. the distance from your desk to the teacher's desk _____

2. how far someone can drive in two hours _____

Circle the letter of the better estimate.

3. height of a telephone pole

   a. 5 m   **b.** 5 km

4. distance from Los Angeles to San Diego

   a. 200 m   **b.** 200 km

Spiral Review (Chapter 7, Lessons 2 and 3) **KEY** NS 2.2, AF 1.5

Find the missing number.

5. 6 × 8 = _____.

6. 7 × _____ = 42

7. There were 7 people fishing from a pier. Each of them caught 8 fish. How many fish did they catch in all? _____

Name _____ Date _____

Convert Metric Units of Length

Use the table to answer the problems.

1. The blue whale has a length equal to 2,500 cm. Which type of whale has a length equal to 1,300 cm?

   _____

2. What is the length of a minke whale expressed in centimeters?

   _____

3. Tiara is 160 cm tall. Which whales have a length that is 10 times Tiara's height?

   _____

4. A marine biologist was keeping track of a fin whale that was 80 cm longer than the average. What was the length of the fin whale to the nearest meter?

   _____

5. What is the length of a right whale in centimeters if it is 50 cm shorter than average?

   _____

6. A killer whale was spotted at a distance that happened to be 100 times the length of the whale. About how many kilometers away was the whale?

   _____

Type of Whale	Average Male Adult Length
Blue Whale	25 m
Right Whale	20 m
Sei Whale	16 m
Humpback Whale	13 m
Minke Whale	9 m
Fin Whale	20 m
Sperm Whale	16 m
Killer Whale	10 m

Hands On: Line Segments and Angles

CA Standards
MG 2.4, MG 2.0

 This figure is part of a straight line. It has a beginning and an end. It is a **line segment**.

Tell whether each figure is a *right angle*, *less than a right angle*, or *greater than a right angle*.

1.

2.

3.

4.

_____   _____   _____   _____

_____

Tell whether each pair of line segments is *parallel* or *not parallel*.

5.

6.

7.

8.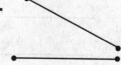

_____   _____   _____   _____

Spiral Review (Chapter 7, Lessons 1 and 3) **KEY NS 2.2, AF 1.5**

Multiply.

9.   8
    $\times 7$

10.   7
     $\times 6$

11. The row for 3 in the multiplication table looks like this: 3, 6, 9, ___, 15, ___, 21, 24, 27, 30. What are the missing products?

_____

Homework and Problem Solving
77
Use with text pp. 190–191

Hands On: Line Segments and Angles

CA Standards
MG 2.4, MG 2.0

Solve. Tell which part(s) of the house answer each question.

1. What are two pairs of parallel lines?

_____

_____

_____

_____

2. What are two lines that are not parallel?

_____

_____

_____

_____

3. Where do you see right angles?

_____

_____

_____

_____

4. Where do you see angles that are less than a right angle?

_____

_____

_____

5. Where do you see angles that are greater than a right angle?

_____

_____

6. How many right angles are there in all? (Hint: Put a dot at each right angle, then count them.)

_____

_____

Plane Figures

CA Standards
MG 2.0, **KEY** MG 2.1

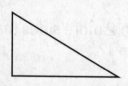 A **polygon** is a closed figure that has three or more line segments.

Tell whether the figure is a polygon. If it is, write its name.

1.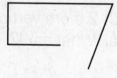

2.

3.

4.

_____

_____

_____

_____

5.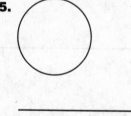

6.

7.

_____

_____

_____

_____

_____

_____

Spiral Review (Chapter 3, Lesson 2) **KEY AF 1.1**

Write <, > or = in the ◯ **.**

8. $24 + 18$ ◯ $30 + 14$

9. $33 + 31$ ◯ $17 + 47$

10. Kevin and Gerry have the same number of freckles as Caitlin and Mary. Complete the equation to show this fact.

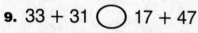

$105 + 7 = 83 + \square$

_____

Name ______________________ Date ______________

Plane Figures

CA Standards
MG 2.0, KEY MG 2.1

Solve each riddle.

1. I am a polygon with 3 sides. What am I?

____

2. I am a polygon with 2 more sides than a triangle. What am I?

____

3. I am a polygon with 8 vertices. What am I?

____

4. I am a polygon with 2 more vertices than a quadrilateral. What am I?

____

5. I am a polygon with twice as many sides as another polygon. I have fewer than 8 sides. What am I?

____

6. I am a closed plane figure but I am **not** a polygon. What am I?

____

Hands On: Sort Triangles and Quadrilaterals

CA Standards
KEY MG 2.2, **KEY** MG 2.3

 This triangle has all sides the same length.

Draw a figure to match the description. Use a ruler to help you.

1. A triangle with 1 right angle

2. A quadrilateral with at least 1 pair of parallel sides

3. A triangle with sides all the same length

4. A quadrilateral with all sides the same length

Spiral Review (Chapter 7, Lesson 3) **KEY NS 2.2, AF 1.5**

Multiply.

5. $\begin{array}{r} 9 \\ \times 7 \\ \hline \end{array}$

6. $\begin{array}{r} 6 \\ \times 10 \\ \hline \end{array}$

7. $6 \times 1 = 6$, $6 \times 2 = 12$, $6 \times 3 = 18$ ... What pattern do you see?

Hands On: Sort Triangles and Quadrilaterals

CA Standards
KEY MG 2.2, **KEY** MG 2.3

Solve each problem.

1. What is the fewest sides of the same length a quadrilateral can have?

_____

2. What is the most sides of the same length a quadrilateral can have?

_____

3. What is the fewest number of right angles a triangle can have?

_____

4. What is the most right angles a triangle can have?

_____

5. How many parallel lines can a triangle have?

_____

6. What is the most right angles a quadrilateral can have?

_____

Triangles

CA Standard
KEY MG 2.2

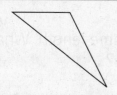

The triangle has three sides of different lengths.
It is a **scalene triangle.**

Name the triangle. Write *equilateral, isosceles, right,* or
scalene. Triangles can have more than one name. Use a ruler.

1.
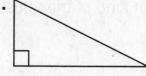

_____

_____

2.

_____

_____

3.

_____

_____

4.
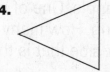

_____

_____

5.

_____

_____

6.

_____

_____

Spiral Review (Chapter 7, Lesson 4) **KEY AF 1.5**

Find the product. Multiply the factors in parentheses first.

7. $(3 \times 2) \times 5 =$ _____

8. $8 \times (5 \times 2) =$ _____

9. There are 3 cages. There are 2 hamsters in each cage. Each hamster
has 4 legs. How many legs are there in all?

_____

Homework and Problem Solving

83

Use with text pp. 198–199

Triangles

CA Standard
KEY MG 2.2

Solve each riddle.

1. I have 3 sides of different lengths. What kind of triangle am I?

   _____

2. I have 2 sides the same length. What kind of triangle am I?

   _____

3. I am an equilateral triangle. One side is 3 inches long. How long are my other two sides?

   _____

4. I was a square, but I got cut in half diagonally. What kind of triangles am I now?

   _____

5. I am an equilateral triangle. Two of my sides are each 1 yard long. How many **inches** long is my third side?

   _____

6. I am an isosceles triangle. One of my sides is 24 inches long. How many **feet** long is my other side that is the same length?

   _____

Quadrilaterals

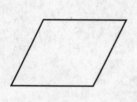

The figure has four sides.
It is a **quadrilateral**.

Its opposite sides are parallel.
It is a **parallelogram**.

Tell whether the figure is a quadrilateral. If it has special names, write them.

1.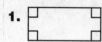

_____

_____

2. ▢

3. ▱

4. ◯

5.

_____

_____

6.

7.

8.

Spiral Review (Chapter 8, Lesson 2) **MG 1.1**

Choose the unit you would use to measure. Write *inch*, *foot*, *yard*, or *mile*.

9. the length of your kitten's tail

_____

10. the distance from the ground to the roof of your school

_____

11. Which is a better estimate for how high you can jump, 2 feet or 2 yards?

_____

Quadrilaterals

CA Standard
KEY MG 2.3

Use the map to solve each problem.

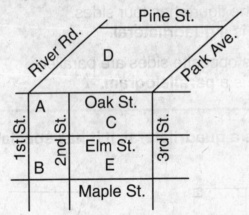

1. What kind of quadrilateral is block A?

_____

2. What kind of quadrilateral is block C?

_____

3. Blocks A and B together make what kind of quadrilateral?

_____

4. Blocks C and E together make what kind of quadrilateral?

_____

5. Oak St., 3rd St., Maple St., and 1st St. form the sides of what kind of quadrilateral?

_____

6. Pine St., Park Ave., Oak St., and River Rd. form the sides of what kind of quadrilateral?

_____

Homework and Problem Solving
86
Use with text pp. 200–203

Problem Solving: Draw a Picture

Alvin has a board that is 6 inches long. He cuts the board into 3 equal pieces. Then he cuts each of those pieces in half. How long is each piece of Alvin's board?

Step ① Draw a picture of Alvin's original board. Then divide it into equal thirds.

Step ② Draw another picture showing each piece divided in two and note the inches.

Solution: Each piece of Alvin's board is 1 inch long.

Draw a picture to solve each problem.

1. Wendy cut a ribbon into 11 pieces to make bows. How many cuts did she make?

_____

2. Betty cut a 24-inch wooden board into 4 equal pieces. Then she cut each piece into 2 equal pieces. How many pieces of wood did Betty have in the end? How long was each piece?

_____

3. Dorothy has a loaf of bread that is 12 inches long. She cuts the loaf in half. Then she cuts each half into 3 equal slices. How many slices of bread does she have? How thick is each slice?

_____

Spiral Review (Chapter 7, Lesson 3) **KEY NS 2.2**

Find the product.

4. $7 \times 8 =$ _____

5. $6 \times 4 =$ _____

6. Missy is arranging flowers for her party. She has 9 vases. She wants to put 8 roses in each vase. How many roses should she buy? _____

Name _____ Date _____

Problem Solving: Draw a Picture

Draw a picture to help solve each problem.

1. Amelia made her vegetable garden in the shape of a square. Each side is 32 feet long. Amelia walked around her garden. How many feet did she walk in all?

_____

_____

2. Rick has a board that is 10 feet long. He cuts it into 5 equal pieces. How long is each piece? How many cuts did he make?

_____

_____

3. Rhonda is building birdhouses for her nephews. For the birdhouse perch, she cuts a 30-inch wooden dowel into 3 equal pieces. Then she cuts each of those pieces in half. How many pieces of wood does she have for the birdhouse perches? How long is each piece?

_____

_____

_____

4. Jonathan has a piece of string that is 16 inches long. He cuts it into 4 equal pieces. Then he cuts each piece in half. How many pieces of string does he have now? How long is each piece?

_____

_____

_____

5. Sherry has 2 right triangles. Each triangle has 2 sides that are equal in length. If Sherry put the triangles together can she form a square? A rectangle?

_____

_____

6. Eddie made a beaded necklace for his mother. Every third bead is blue. Every seventh bead is green. All the remaining beads are white. There are 20 beads in all. How many beads are blue? Green? White?

_____

_____

_____

Hands On: Explore Perimeter

CA Standards
KEY MG 1.3, MG 1.1

Choose three objects in your home. Trace a face of each object. Then estimate the perimeter of the face. Record your estimates. Then measure the perimeter to the nearest inch.

Object	Estimate	Measurement
A comic book	The comic book looks like it is about 30 inches around. **My estimate is 30 inches.**	Run a string around the perimeter of the comic book. Measure with a ruler. **The perimeter of the comic book is 32 inches.**
1.		
2.		
3.		

Spiral Review   (Chapter 9, Lesson 2) MG 2.0, KEY MG 2.1

Tell whether the figure is a polygon. If it is, write its name.

4.

_____

5.

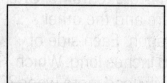

_____

6. Jessica's house has one window in each wall. If her house is the shape of a pentagon, how many windows are there?

_____

Hands On: Explore Perimeter

CA Standards
KEY MG 1.3, MG 1.1

Solve each problem.

1. Yolanda wants to buy a frame for her school photo. To estimate its perimeter, she uses 24 toothpicks to surround the photo. Each toothpick is about 2 inches long. About how many inches long is the perimeter of Yolanda's school photo?

   _____

2. Jamie wants to make a frame for a postcard. To measure its perimeter, he wraps a string around the edges of the postcard. What should he do next to find the perimeter of the postcard in inches?

   _____

   _____

3. Connie is making a wooden frame for a painting. Should she estimate its perimeter with paper clips or measure its perimeter with a ruler? Explain your choice.

   _____

   _____

4. **Predict** An art supply store sells photograph frames in 5 sizes. The perimeters of the first three frames are 20 inches, 24 inches, and 28 inches. If this pattern continues, what are the perimeters of the next two frames likely to be?

   _____

   _____

5. Frank has two mirrors to frame. One mirror is a square and the other mirror is an octagon. Each side of both mirrors is 5 inches long. Which mirror's frame will need more wood?

   _____

   _____

6. Edie wants to measure the perimeter of a square clock face. She has one piece of string that does not fit around the entire perimeter and a ruler. How can she estimate the perimeter?

   _____

   _____

Find Perimeter

CA Standards
KEY MG 1.3, MG 1.0

Find the perimeter of each figure.

Example	Add the lengths of the sides.
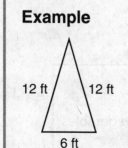 12 ft 12 ft 6 ft	$12 + 12 + 6 = \blacksquare$ $24 + 6 = 30$ **Solution: The perimeter is 30 ft.**

1.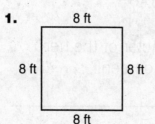

8 ft 8 ft 8 ft 8 ft

_____

2.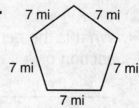

7 mi 7 mi 7 mi 7 mi 7 mi

_____

3.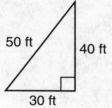

50 ft 40 ft 30 ft

_____

4.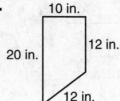

10 in. 12 in. 20 in. 12 in.

_____

5.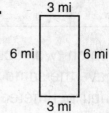

3 mi 6 mi 6 mi 3 mi

_____

6.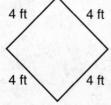

4 ft 4 ft 4 ft 4 ft

_____

7.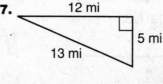

12 mi 5 mi 13 mi

_____

8.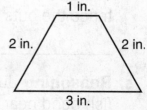

1 in. 2 in. 2 in. 3 in.

_____

Spiral Review (Chapter 8, Lesson 3) MG 1.1

Choose the better estimate.

9. Width of a doorframe: 100 cm or 100 m _____

10. Length of a blackboard: 10 m or 10 cm _____

11. Thom measures the length of his skateboard in millimeters and in centimeters. Will there be more millimeters or centimeters? Explain.

_____

Find Perimeter

CA Standards
KEY MG 1.3, MG 1.0

The diagram below shows Julie's plan for her garden. Use the diagram to solve Problems 1–6. Show your work.

1. What is the perimeter of the herb section of Julie's garden?

   _____

2. What did Julie plant in the largest section in her garden? What is the perimeter of that section?

   _____

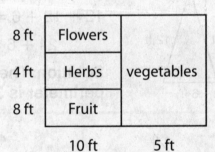

3. Which two sections of her garden have the same perimeter? What is their perimeter?

   _____

4. **Multistep** If each foot of fencing costs $3, how much will it cost to fence the outside of the garden?

   _____

5. **Reasoning** Julie plans to build a fish pond near her garden. The pond will be in the shape of an equilateral triangle. Its perimeter will be 12 feet. What will be the length of each side of the fish pond?

   _____

6. Suppose Julie decides to install a fence around just the vegetables and the herbs. What would be the perimeter of the fence?

   _____

Hands On: Explore Area

CA Standard
KEY MG 1.2

Estimate the area of each figure. Each □ = 1 square unit.

Example   Count the shaded squares.

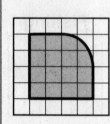

There are about 15.

Solution: The area is about 15 square units.

1.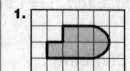

_____

2.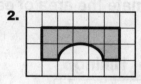

_____

3.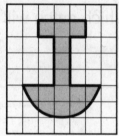

_____

4.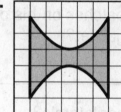

_____

5.

_____

Spiral Review   (Chapter 9, Lesson 2) **MG 2.0, KEY MG 2.1**

Tell whether the figure is a polygon. If it is, write its name.

6.

7.

8. Max wants to build a quadrilateral fence. What are some of the shapes he can build the fence in?

_____

_____

_____

Name _____ Date _____

Hands On: Explore Area

CA Standard
KEY MG 1.2

The figures in Problem 1 show merit patches that Phil earned at camp.
Estimate the area of each patch. Each □ = 1 square unit.

1.

Hiking	Rock Climbing	Canoeing	Fishing
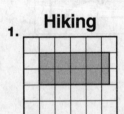	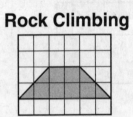	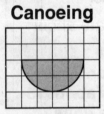	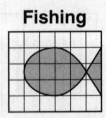

_____ _____ _____ _____

2. Phil plans to sew all his merit patches on his camp jacket. Which patch will
cover the largest space on his jacket?

_____

3. Which of Phils patches are quadrilaterals?

_____

4. Suppose Phil earns two canoeing patches. If he sews them next to each other, what
shape can they form? About how many square units of his jacket will that shape
cover?

_____

5. To see what the mountain climbing patch looks like, draw two line segments
on the rock climbing patch to change it to a triangle. Then estimate the area of
the mountain climbing patch.

_____

6. Phil wants to create a new patch by combining two existing patches and
creating a hexagon. Which two patches can he combine to create a hexagon?
What would be the area of the hexagon?

_____

_____

Find Area

Find the area of each figure. Label your answer in square units. Each ☐ or ⋮ = 1 square unit.

Example Count the square units. There are 9.

Solution: The area is 9 square units.

1.

_____

2.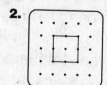

_____

3.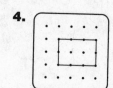

_____

4.

_____

5.

_____

6.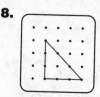

_____

7.

_____

8.

_____

Spiral Review   (Chapter 9, Lesson 2) MG 2.0, KEY MG2.1

Tell whether the figure is a polygon. If so, write its name.

9.

_____

10.

_____

11. Dara is trying to determine whether a figure is a polygon or not. Her teacher told her that the figure is closed, but nothing about the shape of the figure. What else must Dara know to be sure if the figure is a polygon?

_____

Name _____ Date _____

Find Area

CA Standard
KEY MG 1.2

Use the diagram to solve each problem. Show your work.

1. The diagram at the right shows the design of a tiled patio. The patio surrounds a fountain in Jefferson Park. Each tile on the patio covers 1 square foot. What is the area of the patio, in square feet?

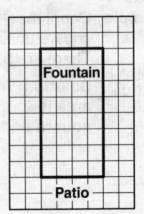

_____

2. Which has the greater area, the patio or the fountain? How much greater, in square feet?

_____

3. The city is replacing the tiles on the patio around the fountain next year. Each tile costs $4. How much will it cost to replace all the tiles?

_____

4. The new patio will have alternating black and white tiles. How many of each color tile should the city planners buy?

_____

5. Suppose the city adds a border of blue tiles around the outside of the patio. The border will be 1 tile wide. The blue tiles are the same size as the tiles on the patio. How many tiles will be needed to make the border?

_____

6. Suppose the city decides to reduce the area of the fountain to 5 square units. By how many units would the area of the patio increase?

_____

Problem Solving: Find a Pattern

CA Standards
MR 1.1, AF 2.2

Mona used 1-inch tiles to make the pattern on the right.
A 1-inch tile measures 1 inch on each side.

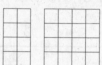

Suppose she continues the pattern. What will be the perimeter of the fifth figure?

Step 1 Recognize the pattern. Each figure has 2 times the number of tiles than the one before it.

Step 2 Extend the pattern to the 4th and 5th figures and then measure the perimeter.

Solution: The perimeter for the 5th figure will be 16 inches.

Find a pattern to solve each problem.

1. Frank made the pattern shown below using 1-inch tiles.

   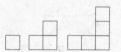

   Suppose he continues his pattern. What will be the perimeter of the sixth figure in his pattern?

   _____

2. Terry made the pattern shown below. Each □ = 1 square unit.

   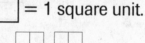

   If she continues the pattern, what will the area of the fifth figure be?

   _____

3. Juan made the pattern below with rectangles that are 2 inches long and 1 inch wide.

   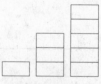

   What will the perimeter of the fifth figure be, if the pattern continues?

   _____

Spiral Review (Chapter 3, Lesson 2) MG 2.2

Tell whether the figure is a polygon. If it is, write its name.

4.

5.

6. A nonagon is a polygon with nine sides. Draw a nonagon.

_____ _____

Problem Solving: Find a Pattern

CA Standards
MR 1.1, AF 2.2

Find a pattern to solve each problem.

1. Hope used 1-inch tiles to make a pattern. The first figure has 1 tile, the second figure has two tiles side by side, and the third figure has three tiles side by side. If she continues her pattern, what will the perimeter of the fifth figure be?

_____

2. Marc made a pattern using square tiles. The first figure is 1 tile. The second figure is 3 tiles stacked in a column. The third figure is 5 tiles stacked in a column. What would the area of the sixth figure in his pattern be?

_____

3. Ellen created a pattern using triangles with 1 inch per side. If she continues the pattern, what will be the perimeter of the seventh figure?

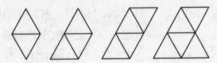

_____

4. Hank made a pattern using rectangles that were 2 inches long and 1 inch wide. If the pattern continues what will be the perimeter of the next figure?

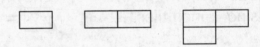

_____

5. If Danielle continues the pattern with 1-inch squares, what will the perimeter of the ninth figure be?

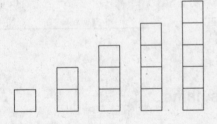

_____

6. Ling began the pattern below. She used squares with 1-inch sides and triangles with a 1-inch base and 2 inches on each side. If the final figure is to look like a star, which figure will be the last and what is its perimeter?

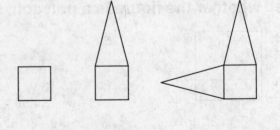

_____

Hands On: Build Solids

The solid below has 6 square faces.

It is a cube.

Name the solid figure that has the faces shown.

1. □ □ ▢ ▢ ▢ ▢

2.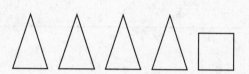

_____ _____

Write *true* or *false* for each. If false, rewrite the statement to make it true.

3. A cube has 8 vertices.

4. A cube has 8 edges.

_____ _____

Spiral Review (Chapter 9, Lesson 4) **KEY** MG 2.2

For problems 5–6, name the triangle. Write *equilateral*, *isosceles*, *right*, or *scalene*. Use a ruler.

5.

6.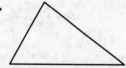

_____ _____

7. A triangle has 1 right angle and 2 equal sides. What two words describe this triangle?

_____

Name _____   Date _____

Hands On: Build Solids

CA Standards
MG 2.0, MG 2.5

Solve. Use the figures below.

    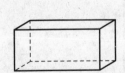

1. I have 6 faces. They are all squares. What solid figure am I?

_____

2. I have 1 face that is a square and 4 faces that are triangles. What solid figure am I?

_____

3. I have 6 faces. Some faces are squares and some are rectangles. What solid figure am I?

_____

4. I am a solid figure that can be made of two cubes put together. What am I?

_____

5. I am a solid figure with 8 edges and 5 vertices. What am I?

_____

6. I am a solid figure with 6 faces, 8 vertices, and 12 edges. My edges are not the same length. What am I?

_____

Solid Figures

CA Standard
MG 2.5

Name the solid figure that the object looks like.

The figure is round.
It has no edges.

It is a sphere.

1.

_____

2.

_____

3.

_____

4.

_____

5.

_____

6.

_____

Spiral Review (Chapter 8, Lesson 4) MG 1.1

**Choose the unit you would use to measure each.
Write *mm*, *cm*, *m*, or *km*.**

7. length of your toothbrush

_____

8. distance from your home to school

_____

9. Billy estimated the length of a pencil as 15 cm. Lester estimated the length of a pencil as 15 mm. Which is the better estimate?

_____

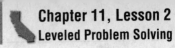
Solid Figures

CA Standards
MG 2.5, MG 2.6

Use the objects below to solve problems 1–5.

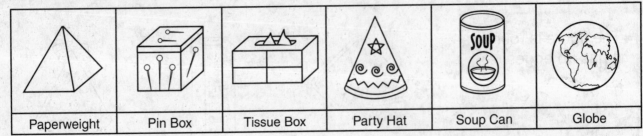

Paperweight	Pin Box	Tissue Box	Party Hat	Soup Can	Globe

1. Which objects will NOT roll smoothly?

_____

_____

2. Name the solid figure that matches the soup can.

_____

3. Chantall says that the pin box is a cube. Emily say that it is a rectangular prism. Who is right? Explain your choice.

_____

_____

_____

_____

4. Which objects have faces that are circles?

_____

5. Meg stacked a cube onto a rectangular prism, and a cylinder on top of the cube. Which 3 objects did she use?

_____

_____

6. The picture below shows an unfolded cardboard container. The dotted lines show where to fold. When the container is folded, what solid figure will its shape be?

_____

Name _____ Date _____

Hands On: Explore Volume

CA Standards
KEY MG 1.2, MG 1.0

Estimate the volume of the figure. Then build it with cubes. Write the estimate and the number of cubes you used.

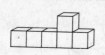
An estimate for the volume is 5 cubic units.

The figure is made with 6 cubes.

The volume is 6 cubic units.

1.

Estimate: _____ unit cubes

Exact: _____ unit cubes

2.

Estimate: _____ unit cubes

Exact: _____ unit cubes

3.

Estimate: _____ unit cubes

Exact: _____ unit cubes

4.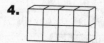

Estimate: _____ unit cubes

Exact: _____ unit cubes

5.

Estimate: _____ unit cubes

Exact: _____ unit cubes

Spiral Review (Chapter 9, Lesson 5) **KEY** MG 2.3

For problems 6–7, tell whether the figure is a quadrilateral. If it has special names, write them.

6.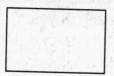

_____

7.

_____

8. A figure has 2 sets of parallel sides and 4 right angles. All of the sides are the same length. What are the 3 names for the figure?

_____

Name _____ Date _____

Hands On: Explore Volume

CA Standards
KEY MG 1.2, MG 1.0

For Problems 1–4, use the unit cubes shown in each box to
estimate the volume of that box. Then use your estimates
to solve Problems 5–6.

1. Fawn's Box

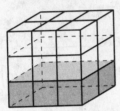

_____

2. Micah's Box

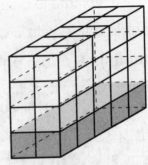

_____

3. Joey's Box

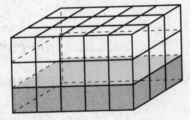

_____

4. Rachel's Box

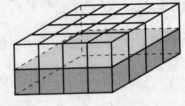

_____

5. Whose box has the greatest
    volume? Whose box has the least
    volume?

_____

6. Can two of Fawn's boxes fit inside
    any of the other boxes? If yes,
    which one?

_____

Find Volume

Find the voume of the figure. Each = 1 cubic unit.

> Remember to count the cubes that are hidden.
>
>
>
> **The volume is 12 cubic units.**

1.

_____

2.

_____

3.

_____

4.

_____

5.

_____

6.

_____

7.

_____

8.

_____

Spiral Review (Chapter 10, Lesson 2) **KEY** MG 1.3, MG 1.0

For problems 9–10, find the perimeter of the figure.

9.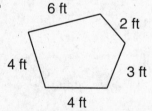

6 ft
2 ft
4 ft
3 ft
4 ft

_____

10.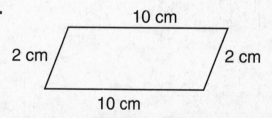

10 cm
2 cm
2 cm
10 cm

_____

11. Molly's bedroom is a square. One side is 11 feet. What is the perimeter of Molly's bedroom?

_____

Name _____ Date _____

Find Volume

Solve each problem. Use the figure below.

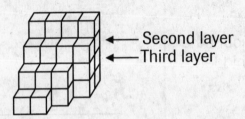

← Second layer
← Third layer

1. How many unit cubes are in the top layer?

_____

2. How many unit cubes are in the second layer?

_____

3. How many unit cubes are in the third layer?

_____

4. How many unit cubes are in the bottom layer?

_____

5. What is the volume of the figure?

_____ cubic units

6. How many cubes are hidden?

_____

Problem Solving: Perimeter, Area, or Volume?

CA Standards
KEY MG 1.0, MR 2.4

Jake wants to build a box with at least 6 cubit units of space inside. Which of these plans should he follow?

Step 1 Count the number of cubic units in each figure.

Figure A has 4 cubic units.

Figure B has 6 cubic units.

Step 2 Compare each total to the number Jake needs for his box.

$4 < 6$ $6 = 6$

Solution: Figure B is the plan that Jake should follow to build the box. He has found the volume.

Solve each problem. Tell whether you found perimeter, area, or volume.

1. Marge wants to build a doghouse for her dog. She needs a space with at least 10 square units of floor. Will the plan at the right work? Why or why not?

_____

2. Tomas wants to place a border of stones around his flower garden. He drew the sketch of the garden at the right. How many units of stones are needed?

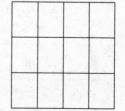

1 unit

2 units

_____

Spiral Review   (Chapter 10, Lesson 2 KEY MG 1.3, MG 1.0)

Find the perimeter of each figure.

3.
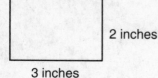
2 inches

3 inches

4.
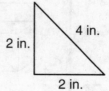
4 in.
2 in.
2 in.

5. A walkway is 12 feet long and 3 feet wide. What is the perimeter of the walkway?

_____   _____   _____

Name _____ Date _____

Problem Solving: Perimeter, Area, or Volume?

CA Standards
KEY MG 1.0, MR 2.4

Solve each problem involving perimeter, area, or volume.

1. Lena wants to put a cloth border around her planter. It is a perfect square with 4 units on each side. How many units of cloth will she need for the border?

_____

2. There are 4 square units in a row of carpeting, and 3 rows in Daniel's finished basement. How many square units of carpeting does he need to cover it completely?

_____

3. Maria has a 24 cubic-unit tank for her snake. It has outgrown the tank and needs another 8 cubic units. Is the tank shown below large enough for her snake?

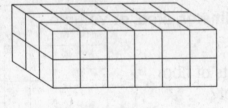

_____

_____

_____

4. Harry helps with a town beautification project. He wants to plant rows of flowers around median dividers that look like the triangle below. If there are three dividers of the same size as the one shown, how many units of flowers will Harry need to plant?

_____

5. Fred wants to put square tiles on the floor of his bathroom shown below. He has $85 to spend. Each tile square costs $7. Does he have enough money? Explain.

_____

_____

6. Sally has a box 6 units high, 4 units wide, and 4 units long. How many cubes like the one below can she fit in the box?

_____

Hands On: Model Division

CA Standards
NS 2.0, MR 2.3

Divide. Make a drawing. Then complete the division sentence.

	Number of Counters	Number of Equal Groups	Number in Each Group	Division Sentence
	10	2	5	$10 \div 2 = 5$
1.	8	2	_____	$8 \div 2 =$ _____
2.	9	3	_____	$9 \div 3 =$ _____
3.	12	4	_____	$12 \div 4 =$ _____
4.	15	_____	3	$15 \div 3 =$ _____
5.	12	_____	2	$12 \div 2 =$ _____
6.	20	_____	5	$20 \div 5 =$ _____

Spiral Review   (Chapter 1, Lessons 3 and 4) **KEY NS 1.1, NS 1.3, NS 1.5**

Solve.

7. What is the value of the underlined digit in 8,3̲05? _____

8. Write 392 in expanded form. _____

9. Isabel picked up 105 pieces of trash on Beach Cleanup Day.
What did she write to show the 0 in 105 using expanded form? _____

Hands On: Model Division

CA Standards
NS 2.0, MR 2.3

Solve each problem.

Show your work.

1. Ben has 15 counters. To divide them into equal groups, Ben draws the circles below. Draw dots to show the number of counters Ben should place in each circle.

2. Write a division sentence to describe your completed picture from Problem 1. Label each part of the sentence as *number of counters, number of groups,* or *number in each group.*

_____

_____

3. Sarah and Cal each have 12 counters. Sarah places an equal number of her counters in each of 3 circles. Cal places an equal number of his counters in each of 4 circles. Who has more counters in each circle?

_____

4. Jake has an even number of counters. Carlos has an odd number of counters. How many more counters do they need to divide the combined total into an even number of groups?

_____

5. Latifa has 8 counters. Steve has twice as many counters as Latifa. They combine their counters and then share them equally. How many counters do they each get?

6. Adriana and Kyle have the same number of counters. They combine them with Terry's counters and divide the total into 3 equal groups. If Adriana had 9 counters, what is the least number of counters Terry could have had?

_____

Relate Division and Multiplication

CA Standards
KEY NS 2.3, MR 3.2

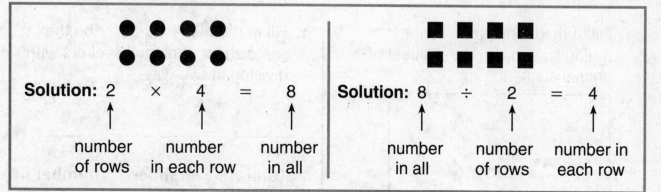

Solution: 2 × 4 = 8

↑ number of rows ↑ number in each row ↑ number in all

Solution: 8 ÷ 2 = 4

↑ number in all ↑ number of rows ↑ number in each row

Use the array to complete the number sentence.

1.

4 × _____ = 20

20 ÷ _____ = 5

2. ▲ ▲ ▲ ▲ ▲
▲ ▲ ▲ ▲ ▲

_____ × 5 = 10

_____ ÷ 2 = 5

3.

3 × _____ = 6

6 ÷ _____ = 2

Draw an array for each multiplication sentence. Then write a related division sentence.

4. 4 × 3 = 12

_____

5. 3 × 5 = 15

_____

6. 2 × 8 = 16

_____

Spiral Review (Chapter 9, Lesson 2) **MG 2.0, KEY MG 2.1**

For 7–8, tell whether the figure is a polygon. If it is, write its name.

7. ⬡ _____

8. ▢ _____

9. The fence around a triangular flower bed is 10 feet long on all sides. What type of triangle does the fence form?

_____

Relate Multiplication and Division

CA Standards
KEY NS 2.3, MR 3.2

Answer each question.

1. Fill in the blanks to describe multiplication using this sheet of animal stickers.

_____ × _____ = _____

  ↑   ↑   ↑

number of   number in   total
rows   each row   number

2. Fill in the blanks to describe the same sheet of animal stickers with division in two ways.

_____ ÷ _____ = _____

  ↑   ↑   ↑

total   number   number in
number   of rows   each row

_____ ÷ _____ = _____

  ↑   ↑   ↑

total   number in   number
number   each row   of rows

3. Write 4 different multiplication and division sentences using the numbers 3, 9, and 27.

_____

_____

4. If an array shows a square number, how many multiplication and division sentences can describe the array?

_____

5. Write a division sentence modeled by an array that has 2 more rows than the number in each row.

_____

6. Mary says that the greater the number of counters, the greater the number of different arrays you can form. Give an example that shows that Mary is wrong.

_____

_____

Different Ways to Divide

CA Standard
KEY NS 2.3

Way 1: Use repeated subtraction.	**Way 2:** Make equal groups.	**Way 3:** Use a related multiplication fact.
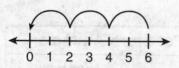		Think: $2 \times$ ■ $= 6$
Solution: $6 \div 2 = 3$	**Solution:** $6 \div 3 = 2$	**Solution:** $6 \div 2 = 3$

Use the pictures or the multiplication facts to find each quotient.

1.

   $8 \div 4 =$ _____

2.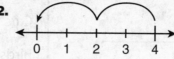

   $4 \div 2 =$ _____

3. ■ ■
   ■ ■
   ■ ■
   ■ ■

   $10 \div 5 =$ _____

Find the quotient. Tell which way you used.

4. $7 \times 2 = 14$

   $14 \div 2 =$ _____

5. $6 \times 2 = 12$

   $12 \div 2 =$ _____

6. $1 \times 2 = 2$

   $2 \div 2 =$ _____

7. $8 \div 2 =$ _____

8. $16 \div 2 =$ _____

9. $10 \div 2 =$ _____

Spiral Review (Chapter 9, Lesson 5) **KEY MG 2.3**

10. What are two names that describe this polygon?

11. Where does a parallelogram get its name?

12. Eric cut out a square piece of paper.

   Which side was longer? _____

Different Ways to Divide

At Paw's Pet Store, 2 animals share each cage. The table
below shows how many animals are in the store now. Find the
quotient. Tell which way you used.

Paw's Pet Store Animals	
Animal	**Number**
Mice	22
Snakes	4
Hamsters	18
Cats	12
Birds	16
Guinea Pigs	10
Rabbits	14
Lizards	6
Crickets	20
Dogs	8

1. How many cages are needed for all
   the birds?

   _____

2. How many cages are needed for all
   the rabbits?

   _____

3. How many more cages are needed
   to hold all the hamsters than to hold
   all the guinea pigs?

   _____

4. Which kind of animal needs twice
   as many cages as all the lizards need?

   _____

5. The pet store uses a total of 6 cages to
   hold two different kinds of animals.
   What animals are they?

   _____

6. If 3 animals shared a cage instead of 2, there
   would be 3 fewer cages for one of the animals.
   Which one?

   _____

Practice Dividing by 2, 5, or 10

$10 \div 2 =$ ■ ■ ■ ■ ■ ■ ■ ■ ■ ■	There are 2 rows with 5 squares in each row. Solution: $10 \div 2 = 5$

Use the array to help you find each quotient.

1. ● ● ● ● ●
   ● ● ● ● ●
   ● ● ● ● ●
   ● ● ● ● ●

   $20 \div 5 =$ _____

2. ● ● ● ● ●
   ● ● ● ● ●
   ● ● ● ● ●

   $15 \div 5 =$ _____

3. ▲ ▲ ▲ ▲ ▲

   $5 \div 5 =$ _____

Divide. Check by multiplying.

4. $40 \div 5 =$ _____

5. $25 \div 5 =$ _____

6. $14 \div 2 =$ _____

7. $2\overline{)6}$

8. $5\overline{)45}$

9. $10\overline{)50}$

10. $10\overline{)30}$

Spiral Review (Chapter 11, Lesson 2) MG 2.5, MG 2.6

Solve.

11. What solid figures make up this object?

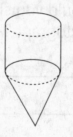

12. What geometric shape is a bowling ball?

_____

_____

13. Andy traced each face of a square pyramid onto a sheet of paper.

   How many, and what shapes did he draw?_____

Name _____ Date _____

Practice Dividing by 2, 5 or 10

CA Standards
KEY NS 2.3, MR 2.0

Use the data in the table below to complete the pictograph at the right. Then use your completed pictograph to solve each problem.

Dog Show Competitors

Dog Breed	Number of Dogs
Poodle	35
German Shepherd	10
Beagle	15
Retriever	20
Terrier	45

Dog Show Competitors

Dog Breed	Number of Dogs
Poodle	
German Shepherd	
Beagle	
Retriever	
Terrier	

Each 🦴 stands for 5 dogs.

1. How many pictures did you draw for poodles? Why?

_____

_____

2. For which dog breed did you draw 4 pictures? Why?

_____

_____

3. Kylie drew 5 pictures for German shepherds on her pictograph because 5 + 5 = 10. What mistake did she make?

_____

_____

4. Last year, there were twice as many beagles in the dog show. How would you show that number on the pictograph? Explain.

_____

_____

5. If the total number of dogs stayed the same but all breeds had the same number of dogs, how many pictures would there be for each breed?

_____

6. Suppose you create a new pictograph using $1\frac{1}{2}$ pictures to show the same number of beagles. What does each picture stand for?

_____

Hands On: Use a Multiplication Table to Divide

CA Standard
KEY NS 2.3

Use the multiplication table to find **42 ÷ 6.** Find the row marked 6.	Move across this row to the column that shows 42.	Look at the number at the top of this column. It is 7.

x	0	1	2	3	4	5	6	7	8	9	10
0	0	0	0	0	0	0	0	0	0	0	0
1	0	1	2	3	4	5	6	7	8	9	10
2	0	2	4	6	8	10	12	14	16	18	20
3	0	3	6	9	12	15	18	21	24	27	30
4	0	4	8	12	16	20	24	28	32	36	40
5	0	5	10	15	20	25	30	35	40	45	50
6	0	6	12	18	24	30	36	42	48	54	60
7	0	7	14	21	28	35	42	49	56	63	70
8	0	8	16	24	32	40	48	56	64	72	80
9	0	9	18	27	36	45	54	63	72	81	90
10	0	10	20	30	40	50	60	70	80	90	100

Solution: $42 \div 6 = 7$

Complete the chart.
Use the multiplication table to help.

		Divisor	Dividend	Quotient
1.	40 ÷ 5			
2.	49 ÷ 7			
3.	36 ÷ 4			
4.	30 ÷ 3			

Spiral Review (Chapter 9, Lesson 5) **KEY MG 2.3**

Identify the geometric shape.

5. What geometric shape has 4 right angles and sides with two different lengths?

_____

6. What quadrilateral has two pairs of parallel sides?

_____

7. Brianna placed two identical square tiles together to form a geometric shape with 4 sides. What shape did she form?

_____

Hands On: Use a Multiplication Table to Divide

Use the multiplication table at the right to solve each problem.

1. What two division sentences describe the row and column in the multiplication table that meet at 42?

_____

_____

×	0	1	2	3	4	5	6	7	8	9	10
0	0	0	0	0	0	0	0	0	0	0	0
1	0	1	2	3	4	5	6	7	8	9	10
2	0	2	4	6	8	10	12	14	16	18	20
3	0	3	6	9	12	15	18	21	24	27	30
4	0	4	8	12	16	20	24	28	32	36	40
5	0	5	10	15	20	25	30	35	40	45	50
6	0	6	12	18	24	30	36	42	48	54	60
7	0	7	14	21	28	35	**42**	49	56	63	70
8	0	8	16	24	32	40	48	56	64	72	80
9	0	9	18	27	36	45	54	63	72	81	90
10	0	10	20	30	40	50	60	70	80	90	100

2. What is the dividend in each of your number sentences for Problem 1? Without looking at the multiplication table, how do you know that this dividend appears somewhere else in the table?

_____

3. Nancy says that 0 is written once in every row and column because the quotient of any number divided by 0 is 0. What's wrong with what Nancy says?

_____

_____

4. I am a square number dividend. I am an odd number. I appear more than once in the table. What dividend am I?

_____

5. Suppose the multiplication table also included 11 and 12 as factors. How many more times would 12 appear as a dividend in the table?

_____

6. How many different division problems can you solve with the 10 × 10 multiplication table if you do not include problems with a dividend of 0?

_____

Practice Dividing by 3 or 4

CA Standards
KEY NS 2.3, NS 2.0

Find the quotient.

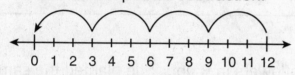

$3)\overline{12}$

You can use repeated subtraction.

0 1 2 3 4 5 6 7 8 9 10 11 12

Count back by 3s to 0.

Solution: $3)\overline{12}^{4}$

1. $3)\overline{9}$ 2. $3)\overline{18}$

3. $3)\overline{3}$ 4. $3)\overline{24}$

Write >, <, or = for each ◯.

5. $5 \times 2 \bigcirc 10 + 5$ 6. $8 \times 3 \bigcirc 8 + 3$ 7. $50 \div 5 \bigcirc 50 - 5$

8. $7 \times 3 \bigcirc 12 \div 2$ 9. $15 - 6 \bigcirc 3 \times 3$ 10. $20 \div 10 \bigcirc 20 - 10$

Spiral Review (Chapter 8, Lesson 2) MG 1.1, MG 1.4

Solve.

11. How many yards are in 6 feet?   12. How many inches are in 2 feet?

_____   _____

13. Jaime was driving with his family to visit an aunt. His father saw a road sign and said "10 more to go." What customary unit of length did Jaime's father most likely leave out of his statement?

_____

Practice Dividing by 3 or 4

CA Standards
KEY NS 2.3, NS 2.0

Solve each problem. Show your work.

1. Mr. Gomez planted 24 tulip bulbs in his garden. He planted the same number of tulips in 3 rows. How many tulips did he plant in each row?

2. In her backyard, Georgia planted 15 sunflowers in 3 pots. She planted the same number of sunflowers in each pot. How many sunflowers are in each pot?

3. Robert bought 12 flowers at the Farmers' Market. He wants to put the same number of flowers in each of the vases shown at right. Draw flowers in the vases to show how Robert could fill the vases.

4. Anne is making 3 bouquets for a wedding. She has 12 gardenias, 30 roses, and 24 lilies. She wants each bouquet to have the same number of each flower. How can she do it?

5. Mick spent a total of $15 on roses and irises. The number of irises he bought is one more than the number of roses he bought. Each flower cost $3. How many roses did he buy? How many irises did he buy?

6. Jia bought some flowers and divided them equally into 3 vases. Then she bought one more flower and was able to divide all the flowers equally into 4 vases. What three different amount of flowers under 30 could Jia have bought to begin with?

Fact Families

CA Standards
KEY NS 2.3, AF 1.2

$5 \times 6 = 30$	5 rows $\times$ 6 in each row $= 30$ (total)	$5 \times 6 = 30$
$6 \times$ _____ $= 30$	6 in each row $\times$ 5 rows $= 30$ (total)	$6 \times 5 = 30$
$30 \div 6 =$ _____	30 (total) $\div$ 6 in each row $= 5$ rows	$30 \div 6 = 5$
$30 \div$ _____ $= 6$	30 (total) $\div$ 5 rows $= 6$ in each row	$30 \div 5 = 6$

Complete the fact family.

1. $4 \times 4 = 16$

$16 \div 4 =$ _____

2. $1 \times 8 = 8$

$8 \times 1 =$ _____

$8 \div$ _____ $= 8$

$8 \div 8 =$ _____

3. $4 \times 7 = 28$

$7 \times$ _____ $= 28$

$28 \div 7 =$ _____

$28 \div$ _____ $= 7$

4. $9 \times 3 = 27$

_____ $\times 9 = 27$

_____ $\div 9 = 3$

$27 \div 3 =$ _____

Spiral Review (Chapter 10, Lesson 4) **KEY** MG 1.2

Find the area of each shape in square units.

5.

6.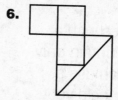

_____   _____

7. Maria made 5 different figures using the same 6 tiles. Do the
figures all have the same area, different areas, or are you unable to tell?

_____

121

Name _____ Date _____

Fact Families

CA Standards
KEY NS 2.3, AF 1.2

Solve each problem.

1. If a fact family has only 2 multiplication and division sentences, what do you know about the product and dividend?

   _____

   _____

   _____

2. Helen says that she remembers what fact families are by thinking about a family with three people in it. How do you think this helps her remember?

   _____

   _____

3. One dividend in my fact family is 18. One of my divisors is twice one of my quotients. What three numbers are in my fact family? How do you know?

   _____

   _____

   _____

4. Samuel wrote the fact family below. What did he do wrong?

Samuel
5 x 2 = 10
2 x 5 = 10
2 x 10 = 20
5 x 10 = 50

   _____

5. How many fact families with a dividend under 100 contain only odd numbers? You can use a multiplication table to help you.

   _____

6. The fact families $2 \times 3 = 6$ and $2 \times 10 = 20$ both contain exactly three different digits. How many other fact families with dividends under 100 contain exactly three different digits? Name one multiplication fact in each of these families.

   _____

   _____

   _____

Practice Dividing by 9

CA Standards
KEY NS 2.3, AF 1.2

Find the factor and quotient.

	You can use a related multiplication fact.	You can use a related division fact.
$9 \times$ _____ $= 27$ $27 \div 9 =$ _____	**Think:** $3 \times 9 = 27$ **Solution:** $9 \times 3 = 27$ $27 \div 9 = 3$	**Think:** $27 \div 3 = 9$ **Solution:** $9 \times 3 = 27$ $27 \div 9 = 3$

Find the factor and quotient.

1. $9 \times$ _____ $= 36$

   $36 \div 9 =$ _____

2. $9 \times$ _____ $= 81$

   $81 \div 9 =$ _____

3. $9 \times$ _____ $= 0$

   $0 \div 9 =$ _____

4. $9 \times$ _____ $= 72$

   $72 \div 9 =$ _____

5. $9 \times$ _____ $= 18$

   $18 \div 9 =$ _____

6. $9 \times$ _____ $= 45$

   $45 \div 9 =$ _____

Spiral Review (Chapter 12, Lesson 2) **KEY** NS 2.3, MR 3.2

Complete the related number sentences.

7. $4 \times \boxed{} = 12$

   $\boxed{} \div 4 = \boxed{}$

8. $\boxed{} \div 7 = 4$

   $4 \times \boxed{} = \boxed{}$

9. A jeweler placed 20 necklaces on 5 different tables. He placed the same number of necklaces on each table. How many necklaces did the jeweler place on each?

   _____

Name _____ Date _____

Practice Dividing by 9

CA Standards
KEY NS 2.3, AF 1.2

Raul did an inventory of all the books in his collection by subject. He displayed his results in the table below. Use the table to solve each problem.

1. Raul might place 9 history books on each shelf of one bookcase. How many shelves will be in that bookcase?

_____

Raul's Book Collection	
Subject of Book	**Number of Books**
History	72
Art	81
Science	54
Travel	63
Fiction	90
Biography	45
Poetry	27
Cooking	36

2. Raul has 9 empty shelves to hold his cookbooks. If he puts the same number of cookbooks on each shelf, how many will be on each shelf?

_____

3. Raul might put an equal number of each kind of book on 9 shelves. How many types of books will have an even number on each shelf?

_____

4. Raul considered combining two of the subjects and placing 9 books on each shelf. It would take 7 shelves to do this. What were the two subjects?

_____

5. Raul fills 9 shelves with his travels, history, and biography books. Each shelf has the same number of each kind of book. How many books are on each shelf?

_____

6. How many books would Raul have to buy if he wanted to have 10 books on each shelf, no matter what the subject?

_____

Problem Solving: Equal Groups Problems

CA Standards
KEY NS 2.3, MR 2.4

Charlie's family eats 4 eggs every morning for breakfast. How many days will a dozen eggs last them?

Way 1

12	÷	4	=	☐
total number of eggs		number of eggs eaten daily		number of days

$12 \div 4 = 3$

Way 2

4	×	☐	=	12
number of eggs in each group		number of groups		total number of eggs

$4 \times 3 = 12$

Solution: The dozen eggs will last Charlie's family 3 days.

Solve each problem using equal groups.

1. Lorna drinks 3 glasses of milk a day. How many glasses will she drink in five days?

   _____

2. Mr. Hernandez gets the newspaper delivered every morning. It costs $3.00 for 6 days delivery. What is the cost of the paper each day?

   _____

3. Phyllis had a piece of ribbon that was 30 inches long. She cut the ribbon into 5 equal pieces. How long is each piece?

   _____

Spiral Review (Chapter 12, Lesson 2) **KEY NS 2.3**

In Problems 4–5, write two related division sentences.

4. $2 \times 4 = 8$ 5. $5 \times 3 = 15$ 6. Hal has 24 baseball cards. He puts 4 cards in each row. How many rows of cards will Hal have?

_____ _____   _____

Name _____ Date _____

Problem Solving: Equal Groups Problems

CA Standards
KEY NS 2.3, MR 2.4,

Solve each problem involving equal groups.

1. The art gallery had 6 rooms. Each room had 8 paintings displayed on its walls. How many paintings were displayed in all?

   _____

2. Every booth in the balcony of the music hall was filled with 100 people. There were 10 booths in each row of the balcony. How many rows were there?

   _____

3. The play had a cast of 13 actors. There were 39 costumes used. If each actor had the same number of costume changes, how many costumes did each actor wear during the play?

   _____

4. The dance recital lasted 135 minutes without an intermission. Each separate group of dancers performed for 15 minutes. How many groups performed during the recital?

   _____

5. In the symphony orchestra there are 4 rows of string players and 4 musicians in each row. There are also 5 rows of brass and reed players with 3 musicians in each row. How many string, brass, and reed players are there in the orchestra?

   _____

6. Gena wants to display her collection of 30 antique puppets in equal-sized rows. What are all the combinations for displaying the puppet collection?

   _____

   _____

   _____

   _____

   _____

   _____

Hands On: Division Rules

CA Standards
NS 2.6, MR 3.0

Example	Example
$5\overline{)5}$	$1\overline{)8}$
When any number except 0 is divided by itself, the quotient is 1.	When any number is divided by 1, the quotient is that number.
Solution	**Solution**
$5\overline{)5}^{\,1}$	$1\overline{)8}^{\,8}$

Divide.

1. $3\overline{)3}$ **2.** $6\overline{)0}$ **3.** $2\overline{)10}$ **4.** $10\overline{)40}$ **5.** $1\overline{)9}$

6. $0 \div 5 =$ _____   **7.** $18 \div 2 =$ _____   **8.** $10 \div 10 =$ _____   **9.** $7 \div 1 =$ _____

10. $0 \div 2 =$ _____   **11.** $12 \div 2 =$ _____   **12.** $7 \div 7 =$ _____   **13.** $9 \div 1 =$ _____

Spiral Review   (Chapter 10, Lesson 4) **KEY** MG 1.2

Estimate the area of the figure. Each ☐ **= 1 square unit.**

14.

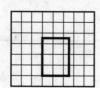

15.

_____   _____

16. Alex wants to put square desks in a storage room. Using grid paper, describe a strategy that he can use in order to determine the maximum number of desks he can fit side-by-side in the storage room.

_____

_____

Name _____ Date _____

Hands On: Division Rules

Solve each problem.

1. Charlie runs a dog-walking service. He has 5 leashes. He uses 1 leash for each dog. How many dogs can Charlie walk at the same time?

_____

2. Charlie walks the dogs the same distance every day. He walks 7 miles every week. How many miles does he walk each day?

_____

3. Charlie had 12 dog biscuits. He gave each of the 12 dogs the same number of biscuits. How many biscuits did he give each dog? How do you know?

_____

_____

4. Charlie planned to split his earnings from Friday with his sister if she helped walk the dogs. He did not give any money to his sister. What can you conclude?

_____

_____

_____

5. Charlie walks 5 dogs. He wants to divide his dog-walking responsibilities evenly among his friends. How many friends must help him walk the dogs?

_____

6. Charlie receives one new leash per week for each dog he walks. If he starts by walking 5 dogs, how many leashes will he have after 3 weeks?

_____

Practice Dividing by 6

CA Standards
KEY NS 2.3, MR 2.4

Example

6)18

:: :: ::
:: :: ::

Make equal groups.

Solution

$\overset{3}{6)18}$

Divide.

1. 6)12   2. 6)30   3. 6)42   4. 6)6

5. 6)24   6. 6)0   7. 6)18   8. 6)36

9. 6)48   10. 6)60   11. 6)42   12. 6)54

13. 24 ÷ 6 = _____   14. 30 ÷ 6 = _____   15. 6 ÷ 6 = _____   16. 48 ÷ 6 = _____

Write >, <, or = for each ◯.

17. 36 ÷ 6 ◯ 4   18. 9 ◯ 27 ÷ 3   19. 32 ÷ 4 ◯ 4 × 9

Spiral Review (Chapter 9, Lesson 2) **KEY MG 2.1, MG 2.0**

Write the name of the polygon.

20. ☐

21.

_____   _____

22. Scott is building a fence around his house. Each corner of the fence needs a post. Which will require more posts, a rectangular fence or a hexagonal fence? How many posts will each require? Explain.

_____

_____

Practice Dividing by 6

CA Standards
KEY NS 2.3, MR 2.4

Mary can fit 6 photographs on each page of her photo albums. The table below shows how many photos she took in each state while visiting the Great Lakes. Use the table to solve each problem.

1. How many pages will Mary fill with the photographs she took in Pennsylvania?

   _____

2. Which state's photos will fill exactly 7 album pages?

   _____

3. Which state's photos will fill twice as many pages as Ohio's will?

   _____

Great Lake State Photographs	
State	**Number of Photographs**
Illinois	54
Indiana	36
Michigan	42
Minnesota	48
New York	60
Ohio	30
Pennsylvania	18
Wisconsin	24

4. How many states' photographs will fill an odd number of pages?

   _____

5. My photos will fill an even number of pages. They will fill fewer pages than Indiana's photos will fill. What state am I?

   _____

6. My photos will fill the same number of pages as the difference between Minnesota's photos and Ohio's photos. Which state am I?

   _____

Practice Dividing by 7

CA Standard
NS 2.3

Example

$7\overline{)35}$

You can use a related multiplication fact.

Think: $7 \times 5 = 35$

$7\overline{)35}^{5}$

Find each quotient.

1. $7\overline{)21}$ 2. $7\overline{)49}$ 3. $7\overline{)0}$

4. $7\overline{)28}$ 5. $7\overline{)56}$ 6. $7\overline{)14}$

7. $7\overline{)42}$ 8. $7\overline{)35}$ 9. $7\overline{)0}$

10. $7\overline{)70}$ 11. $7\overline{)63}$ 12. $7\overline{)28}$

Write +, −, ×, or ÷ for each ◯.

13. $49 \bigcirc 7 = 7$ 14. $8 \bigcirc 6 = 48$ 15. $30 \bigcirc 6 = 24$

16. $6 \bigcirc 6 = 1$ 17. $70 \bigcirc 7 = 10$ 18. $40 \bigcirc 8 = 48$

Spiral Review   (Chapter 11, Lesson 4) **KEY** MG 1.2, MG 1.0

Find the volume of the figure.

19.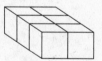

20.

_____   _____

21. If a figure with a volume of a 5 cubic units and a figure with a volume of 14 cubic units were combined, what would the total volume be?

_____

_____

Practice Dividing by 7

CA Standard
KEY NS 2.3

For each dance style, the Step-Up Dance School offers the same number of classes each day. Use the table to solve each problem. (1 week = 7 days) Show your work.

1. How many tap dance classes are taught each day at the school?

_____

2. Brenda wants to take a ballroom dance class on Tuesday. How many classes can she choose from?

_____

3. How many dance styles have an even number of classes each day?

_____

Step-Up Dance School	
Dance Style	**Number of Classes Each Week**
Ballet	70
Salsa	56
Tango	42
Ballroom	63
Tap	28
Flamenco	21
Modern	35
Swing	49

4. Flamenco, salsa, and tango are all Spanish dances. Amanda says that Step-Up Dance School offers exactly 21 Spanish dance classes each day. Is she correct?

_____

5. On Friday, Cara took all of the classes offered in two different styles. Oscar took all of the swing classes offered that day. They both took the same number of classes. Which classes did Cara take?

_____

6. Last week, Emily took all of the modern classes offered on Monday and half of the tango classes offered on Wednesday. How many classes did she take last week?

_____

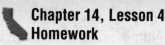
Practice Dividing by 8

CA Standards
KEY NS 2.3, AF 1.2

Example

$8\overline{)40}$

You can use a
related division fact.

Think: $40 \div 5 = 8$

$8\overline{)40}^{5}$

Divide.

1. $8\overline{)0}$

2. $8\overline{)24}$

3. $8\overline{)48}$

4. $8\overline{)16}$

5. $8\overline{)64}$

6. $8\overline{)56}$

7. $8\overline{)32}$

8. $8\overline{)80}$

9. $8\overline{)40}$

10. $8\overline{)8}$

11. $64 \div 8 =$ _____

12. $72 \div 8 =$ _____

13. $32 \div 8 =$ _____

14. $48 \div 8 =$ _____

15. $0 \div 8 =$ _____

16. $24 \div 8 =$ _____

17. $16 \div 8 =$ _____

18. $56 \div 8 =$ _____

Find each missing number.

19. $42 \div 6 = n$

$n =$ _____

20. $8 \times b = 32$

$b =$ _____

21. $a \div 7 = 4$

$a =$ _____

Spiral Review (Chapter 13, Lesson 2) **KEY** NS 2.3, NS 2.0

Divide. Use any strategy.

22. $6 \div 3 =$ _____

23. $32 \div 4 =$ _____

24. Ms. Holmes divided the 24 students in her class into groups of 3.
How many groups did Ms. Holmes make?

Name _____ Date _____

Practice Dividing by 8

CA Standards
KEY NS 2.3, AF 1.2

Display the data given in the table at the left on the pictograph at the right. Then use your completed pictograph to solve each problem.

Brain Teaser Web Site Hits	
Day	Number of Hits
Monday	72
Tuesday	40
Wednesday	32
Thursday	24
Friday	80

Brain Teaser Web Site Hits	
Monday	
Tuesday	
Wednesday	
Thursday	
Friday	
🖱 = 8 hits	

1. How many pictures did you draw for Monday? Why that many?

_____

_____

2. Rosa drew 4 pictures for Thursday on her pictograph because $24 \div 6 = 4$. What mistake did Rosa make?

_____

_____

3. On Saturday, Brain Teaser's Web Site got twice as many hits as on Wednesday. How would you show that number of hits on the pictograph? Explain.

_____

_____

4. Suppose each 🖱 on the pictograph stood for 4 hits. How would the number of pictures you drew for each day change?

_____

_____

6. If Brain Teaser's Web Site received half as many hits in the following week, how would the pictograph change?

5. If there were 83 hits on Friday (instead of 80) how many 🖱 would be on the pictograph? Explain.

_____

_____

_____

_____

_____

Problem Solving: Work Backward

Ron bought 8 grapefruit and 3 cantaloupes. He spent a total of $14. If each cantaloupe costs $2, what was the cost of each grapefruit?

Step ❶ Multiply to find the cost of the 3 cantaloupes.
$2 × 3 = $6

Step ❷ Subtract to find the total cost of the grapefruit.
$14 − $6 = $8

Step ❸ Divide to find the cost of each grapefruit.
$8 ÷ 8 = $1

Solution: Each grapefruit costs $1.

Use a work backward strategy to solve each problem.

1. Gina cut a piece of ribbon into 3 equal pieces. Then she cut 2 inches off one piece to make a piece 3 inches long. How long was Gina's original piece of ribbon?

   _____

2. The Clark family went to the amusement park. The cost for 1 child and 2 adults was $26. If the child's ticket cost $6, what was the cost of each adult ticket?

   _____

3. Tayvon bought a dozen cookies and a bottle of fruit juice to share with his friends. He spent $8 on these items. If the bottle of juice was $2, how much did each cookie cost?

   _____

Spiral Review (Chapter 12, Lesson 4) **KEY NS 2.3, MR 2.0**

Divide. Use any strategy.

4. 40 ÷ 10 _____

5. 24 ÷ 2 _____

6. Marcia has 20 books. She put the same number of books on 5 shelves. How many books did Marcia put on each shelf?

   _____

Problem Solving: Work Backward

Solve each problem by working backward.

1. Indira bought 6 yards of material for drapes and a bag of buttons. She spent a total of $39. If the buttons cost her $3, how much was each yard of material?

_____

2. Max cut a pole into 4 equal pieces. Then he cut 2 inches off one piece of the pole. Then piece left was 4 inches long. How long was the pole to before Max started cutting?

_____

3. Ms. Enrico took 12 of her students on a field trip to the art museum. The cost for 12 students and one adult was $84. If Ms. Enrico's ticket was $12, what did it cost for each student ticket?

_____

4. Marisa bought 6 large cheese pizzas and 3 salads for a party. She paid $99 for everything. If each salad was $5, what was the cost of each pizza?

_____

5. Mr. Leone ate dinner at his favorite restaurant. He had an appetizer, a main course, and dessert. The total bill, minus tax and tip, came to $29. If the main course was $14 and the appetizer cost twice as much as the dessert, how much was the appetizer and how much was the dessert?

_____

_____

6. A total of 121 people came to the school science fair this year. This number is 7 more than twice the number of people who came to last year's science fair. How many people came last year?

_____

Model Fractions

CA Standard
NS 3.0

Write the fraction the model shows.

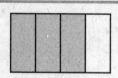

There are 4 parts.

3 parts are shaded.

This model shows $\frac{3}{4}$.

1.

2.

3.

_____ _____ _____

4.

5.

6.

_____ _____ _____

Write the fraction the model shows.

7.   _____

8.   _____

Spiral Review (Chapter 14, Lessons 2–4) **KEY** NS 2.3

Divide.

9. $30 \div 6 = \square$

10. $48 \div 8 = \square$

_____ _____

11. Tommy has 56 marbles and 7 bags. He puts the same number of marbles in each bag. How many marbles are in each bag?

_____

Model Fractions

Solve each problem.

1. The flag of France is shown on the right. What fraction of the flag is red?

   _____

   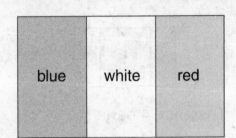

2. The French and Italian flags are the same, except that the Italian flag is green where the French flag is blue. What fraction of the Italian flag is white?

   _____

3. The flag of Greenland is shown on the right. What fraction of the flag is **not** red?

   _____

   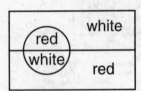

4. The flag of Colombia is shown on the right. About what fraction of the flag is yellow?

   _____

5. The flag of Libya is shown on the right. What fraction of the flag is green?

   _____

6. Erica says that $\frac{1}{5}$ of the national flag of Thailand shown on the right is blue. Why is she wrong?

   _____

   _____

Fractions and Groups

CA Standard
NS 3.0

Write a fraction to name the part of the group that is shaded.

 4 out of 6 squares are shaded. *Four sixths* or $\frac{4}{6}$ are shaded.	

1.

_____

2.

_____

3.

_____

4.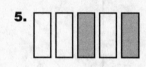

_____

5.

_____

6.

_____

7.

_____

Spiral Review (Chapter 14, Lessons 2–4) **KEY NS 2.3**

Find the missing number.

8. $56 \div \square = 7$

_____

9. $\square \div 6 = 7$

_____

10. Each insect has 6 legs. Howie counted 48 legs. How many insects did he count?

_____

Fractions and Groups

CA Standard
NS 3.0

Use the sheet of stickers at the right to solve the problems.

1. What fraction of the stickers are stars?

_____

2. Which sticker represents the fraction $\frac{2}{15}$?

_____

3. What fraction of the stickers are hearts and stars?

_____

4. What two shapes are the same fraction of the total? What is the fraction?

_____

5. Suppose all the star stickers were removed. What fraction of the stickers would be flowers?

_____

6. What fraction of the stickers are diamonds?

_____

Model Equivalent Fractions

Write *equivalent* or *not equivalent* to describe the fractions in the pair.

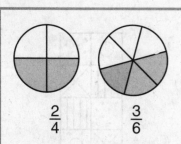

$\frac{2}{4}$ $\frac{3}{6}$

The fractions name the same amount that is colored in each circle. The fractions are **equivalent**.

1.

$\frac{3}{8}$ $\frac{3}{5}$

_____

2.

$\frac{1}{2}$ $\frac{3}{6}$

_____

Use the circles to complete the equivalent fractions.

3.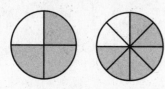

$\frac{3}{4} = \frac{}{8}$

_____

4.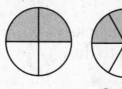

$\frac{}{4} = \frac{3}{6}$

_____

5.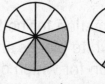

$\frac{4}{10} = \frac{}{5}$

_____

Spiral Review   (Chapter 13, Lesson 4; Chapter 14, Lesson 2) **KEY** NS 2.3

Divide.

6. $24 \div 6 = \square$

_____

7. $63 \div 9 = \square$

_____

8. Adam has 45 crackers and 9 plates. He put the same number of crackers on each plate. How many crackers did he put on each plate?

_____

Model Equivalent Fractions

Beth built a block tower. Use the tower to solve each problem.

1. Which kinds of block represent $\frac{3}{16}$ of the tower?

   _____

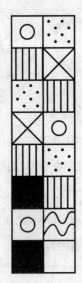

2. The fraction for the zigzag blocks is equivalent to the fraction for which other kind of block?

   _____

3. The blocks with an X make up $\frac{1}{8}$ of the tower. Which other kind of block shows an equivalent fraction?

   _____

4. The fraction for both the dotted blocks and white blocks are equivalent to the fraction for which other block?

   _____

5. The fraction for which kind of block is equivalent to the fraction for the striped blocks?

   _____

6. Beth replaces the white block with a block with dots. The new fraction for the blocks with dots is equivalent to the fraction for which other kind of block?

   _____

Name _____ Date _____

Find Equivalent Fractions

CA Standard
NS 3.1

One half and two fourths name the same amount.

$\frac{1}{2}$ and $\frac{2}{4}$ are **equivalent fractions**.

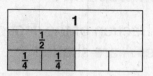

Name the equivalent fractions shown.

1.

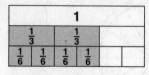

$$\frac{\square}{3} = \frac{\square}{6}$$

_____

2.

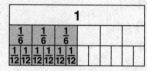

$$\frac{\square}{6} = \frac{\square}{12}$$

_____

3.

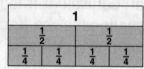

$$\frac{\square}{2} = \frac{\square}{4}$$

_____

4.

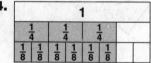

$$\frac{\square}{4} = \frac{\square}{8}$$

_____

5.

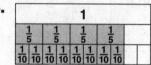

$$\frac{\square}{5} = \frac{\square}{10}$$

_____

6.

$$\frac{\square}{6} = \frac{\square}{12}$$

_____

Spiral Review (Chapter 12, Lesson 3) **KEY NS 2.3**

7. Find the quotient.

$28 \div 4 = \square$

_____

8. Find the quotient.

$35 \div 5 = \square$

_____

9. There are 25 birds' eggs and 5 nests. Each nest has the same number of eggs. How many eggs are in each nest?

_____

Find Equivalent Fractions

CA Standard
NS 3.1

Solve each problem.

1. What fraction of the sections on spinner A are shaded?

   _____

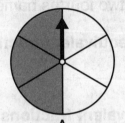

A

2. Shade sections of spinner B to show an equivalent fraction of shaded sections to the fraction shown on spinner A. What is the fraction?

   _____

B

3. Shade sections of spinner C to show an equivalent fraction of shaded sections to the fraction shown on spinner A. What is the fraction?

   _____

C

4. Shade sections of spinner D to show an equivalent fraction of shaded sections to the fraction shown on spinner A. What is the fraction?

   _____

D

5. Divide spinner E into sections. Color sections to show an equivalent fraction to spinners A, B, C, and D.

   _____

E

6. Divide spinner F into sections. Color sections to show an equivalent fraction to spinners A, B, C, D, and E.

   _____

F

Compare Fractions

CA Standard
NS 3.1

Compare the fractions. Write > or < for the ☐ . Use fraction tiles or number lines to help you.

 ☐

$\frac{1}{6}$ ☐ $\frac{1}{5}$

You can use fraction tiles.

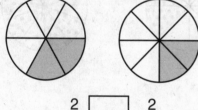

$\frac{1}{6} < \frac{1}{5}$

1. $\frac{2}{8}$ ☐ $\frac{1}{3}$

2.  $\frac{2}{6}$ ☐ $\frac{2}{8}$

3. 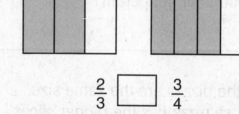 $\frac{2}{3}$ ☐ $\frac{3}{4}$

4. $\frac{1}{8}$ ☐ $\frac{1}{4}$

5. $\frac{1}{10}$ ☐ $\frac{2}{6}$

6. $\frac{3}{4}$ ☐ $\frac{1}{6}$

Spiral Review (Chapter 8, Lesson 2) MG 1.1

Choose the unit you would use to measure each. Write *inch*, *foot*, *yard*, or *mile*.

7. the length of a worm

8. the height of your teacher

_____

_____

9. Ray wants to measure the height of a basketball hoop. Should he use inches or feet?

_____

Compare Fractions

Use the pizzas to solve each problem.

1. What fraction of Brian's pizza has pepperoni? What fraction of Greg's pizza has pepperoni? Whose pizza has a greater fraction of pepperoni?

   _____

2. What fraction of Carol's pizza has pepperoni? What fraction of Nathan's pizza has pepperoni? Whose pizza has a greater fraction of pepperoni?

   _____

3. Whose pizzas have equivalent fractions of pepperoni?

   _____

4. All the pizzas are the same size. Whose pizza has the bigger slices, Janet's or Brian's?

   _____

5. Nathan eats 1 plain slice of his pizza. Now what fraction of his pizza is pepperoni?

   _____

6. Carol eats 2 slices with pepperoni. Now what fraction of her pizza is pepperoni? Is that fraction greater or less than half?

   _____

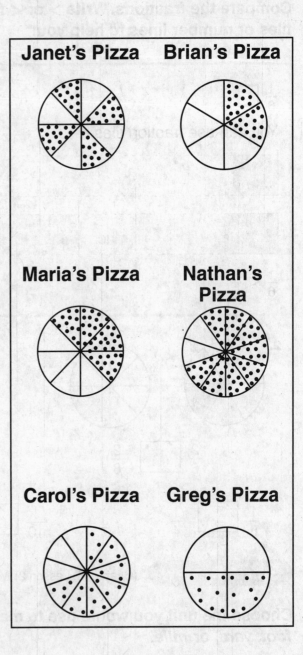

Janet's Pizza   Brian's Pizza

Maria's Pizza   Nathan's Pizza

Carol's Pizza   Greg's Pizza

Too Much Information

You will write a fraction to solve a problem.

Bakery Prices

roll: 10 cents   large loaf of bread: $3

cake: $5   small loaf of bread: $2

pie: $4

Ellie went to the bakery and spent exactly $\frac{1}{2}$ of the money in her pocket. She bought 2 loaves of bread. One was a small loaf of wheat bread. One was a small loaf of oatmeal bread. How much money did Ellie have when she entered the bakery?

Step 1 Decide what information you need to solve the problem. You need to know how many loaves Ellie bought. Also, you need to know the cost of each loaf. To solve the problem, you need to know that Ellie bought 2 small loaves at $2 per loaf.

Step 2 Point out information that is not needed. You do not need to know the flavors of the bread.

Step 3 Now make a plan. You need to find how much money Ellie had when she entered the bakery. You know that she spent exactly $\frac{1}{2}$ of this money. If you figure out how much she spent, you can multiply that number by 2. You can find the sum she spent by adding $2 and $2 or by multiplying $2 times 2.

$2 + $2 = $4 or $2 × 2 = $4
$4 × 2 = $8

Solution: Ellie had $8 when she entered the bakery. The information about flavors of bread was not needed.

Use the information in the example above to solve. Tell what information is not needed to solve the problem.

1. Kevin bought 1 large loaf of bread and a chocolate cake for his aunt's birthday. He paid for them with a $10 bill. What fraction of the $10 did Kevin spend?

_____

_____

Name _____ Date _____

Too Much Information

Solve. Tell what information is not needed to solve the problem.

1. Mr. D'Andrea was the leader of a group of wrestlers running laps around the gym. There were 20 wrestlers running. $\frac{3}{4}$ of the wrestlers were wearing T-shirts, and $\frac{1}{4}$ of the wrestlers were wearing sweatshirts. How many wrestlers were wearing T-shirts?

_____

_____

2. At a supermarket, 6 people were standing in line. Four of them were men, and 2 of them were women. Each of the 6 people were buying 10 items or less. What fraction of the people in line were male?

_____

_____

3. Mrs. Burr has 2 red headbands, 4 red shirts, 3 green headbands, 1 pair of green shoes, and 4 black headbands. What fraction of her headbands are green?

_____

_____

4. Alex's desk at school holds 2 rulers, 1 yellow pencil, 3 red pencils, 1 blue pen, and 4 blue pencils. What fraction of his writing tools are blue?

_____

_____

5. Dawn had 8 bookmarks. Each bookmark showed the designs of 3 flags. $\frac{3}{4}$ of the bookmarks were printed in color, and $\frac{1}{4}$ of the bookmarks were printed in black and gray ink only. If Dawn copied $\frac{1}{2}$ of the flag designs, how many designs did she copy?

_____

_____

6. Trey keeps sports cards in 3 drawers. Each drawer contains exactly 120 cards. In each drawer, $\frac{2}{3}$ of the cards are baseball cards, and $\frac{1}{3}$ of the cards are a mixture of football, hockey, basketball, and soccer cards. If Trey decides to trade $\frac{1}{4}$ of his baseball cards, how many cards will he trade?

_____

_____

Hands On: Add and Subtract Fractions

CA Standards
KEY NS 3.2, MR 2.3

Add $\frac{1}{3} + \frac{1}{3}$. Use fraction tiles to help.

$\frac{1}{3} + \frac{1}{3} = \boxed{}$

| $\frac{1}{3}$ | $\frac{1}{3}$ |

$\frac{1}{3} + \frac{1}{3} = \frac{2}{3}$

When the denominators are the same, keep the denominator and add the numerators.

$\frac{1}{3} + \frac{1}{3} = \frac{2}{3}$

Add. Use fraction tiles to help.

1. $\frac{4}{7} + \frac{2}{7} =$ _____

2. $\frac{1}{4} + \frac{2}{4} =$ _____

3. $\frac{2}{6} + \frac{2}{6} =$ _____

Subtract. Use fraction tiles to help.

4. $\frac{5}{11} - \frac{2}{11} =$ _____

5. $\frac{6}{8} - \frac{3}{8} =$ _____

6. $\frac{2}{3} - \frac{1}{3} =$ _____

Spiral Review (Chapter 11, Lesson 2) **MG 2.5, MG 2.6**

For 7–8, name the solid figure or figures.

7. 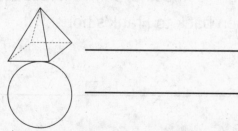 _____

8. 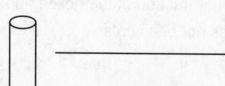 _____

9. Lyle made this object out of blocks. How would you sort the figures in this object?

_____

_____

Add and Subtract Fractions

CA Standards
KEY NS 3.2, MR 2.3

Solve.

1. Will and Betty bought a chocolate chip cookie at the fair. They cut it in 4 equal pieces. Will ate $\frac{1}{4}$ of the cookie and Betty ate $\frac{1}{4}$. What fraction of the cookie did they eat in all?

_____

2. Jack ran $\frac{4}{8}$ of a mile. Mona ran $\frac{3}{8}$ of a mile. How far did they run in all?

_____

3. Mrs. Ortiz added $\frac{3}{4}$ teaspoon of salt and $\frac{3}{4}$ teaspoon of pepper to her stew. Did she add more than, equal to, or less than a teaspoon of both spices combined?

_____

4. The recipe called for a $\frac{3}{4}$ cup of flour and $\frac{1}{4}$ cup of sugar. Together, were the two ingredients more than, equal to, or less than a cup?

_____

5. Hank bought a dozen apples at the farm stand. Sally ate $\frac{2}{12}$ of them, Eddie ate $\frac{3}{12}$, and Sam ate 2 apples. What fraction of the dozen apples has not been eaten?

_____

6. It is $\frac{4}{10}$ of a mile to John's house from Frank's house. How much less than a mile is the distance from Frank's house to John's house and then back to Frank's house?

_____

Name _____ Date _____

Add Fractions

CA Standards
KEY NS 3.2, NS 3.1

$\frac{2}{8} + \frac{4}{8} =$ _____

| $\frac{1}{8}$ | $\frac{1}{8}$ | $\frac{1}{8}$ | $\frac{1}{8}$ | $\frac{1}{8}$ | $\frac{1}{8}$ | | |

When the denominators are the same, add the numerators.

$\frac{2}{8} + \frac{4}{8} = \frac{6}{8}$

Compare $\frac{6}{8}$ and $\frac{3}{4}$.

$\frac{6}{8} = \frac{3}{4}$

Add.

1. | $\frac{1}{7}$ | $\frac{1}{7}$ | $\frac{1}{7}$ | $\frac{1}{7}$ | $\frac{1}{7}$ | | |

$\frac{3}{7} + \frac{2}{7} =$ _____

2. | $\frac{1}{4}$ | $\frac{1}{4}$ | $\frac{1}{4}$ | |

$\frac{2}{4} + \frac{1}{4} =$ _____

Add. Use fractions strips or draw a picture to help you.

3. $\frac{1}{5} + \frac{1}{5} =$ _____

4. $\frac{2}{9} + \frac{3}{9} =$ _____

5. $\frac{5}{12} + \frac{6}{12} =$ _____

Find the sum. Then find a fraction or whole number in the box that is equivalent to the sum.

$1, \frac{2}{3}, \frac{3}{4}, \frac{1}{2}$

6. $\frac{2}{8} + \frac{2}{8} =$ _____

7. $\frac{2}{5} + \frac{3}{5} =$ _____

8. $\frac{2}{6} + \frac{2}{6} =$ _____

Spiral Review (Chapter 11, Lesson 4) **MG 1.2, MG 1.0**

For 9–10, find the volume of the figure.

9.

10.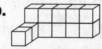

_____   _____

11. A memo cube is 1 cubic unit. Christine packs 6 memo cubes into a box. There is room in the box for 8 more cubes. What is the volume of the box?

_____

Use with text pp. 348–350

Add Fractions

CA Standards
KEY NS 3.2, NS 3.1

For Multicultural Day, students made soups to celebrate their family heritages. Solve each problem about the soups they made.

1. Olga made borscht, a beet soup popular in Russia. Her soup had $\frac{5}{8}$ pound of shredded beets and $\frac{2}{8}$ pound of shredded cabbage. How much beets and cabbage did Olga use in all?

   _____

2. Diego's grandparents are from Mexico. He made chicken tortilla soup with $\frac{3}{5}$ cup of chopped chicken and $\frac{1}{5}$ cup of chopped tortillas. How many cups of chicken and tortillas did he use in all?

   _____

3. Shana made Irish stew with $\frac{3}{4}$ pound of cubed beef and $\frac{1}{4}$ pound of cubed potatoes. How many pounds of beef and potatoes did she use in the stew?

   _____

4. Angela's father is from Italy. She used his recipe to make minestrone soup. The recipe called for $\frac{3}{4}$ cup sliced tomatoes, $\frac{1}{4}$ cup sliced carrots, and $\frac{1}{2}$ cup sliced zucchini. Did she use more or less than 1 cup of sliced vegetables? Explain.

   _____

5. Chris's aunt makes a fruit salad. She uses $\frac{1}{2}$ cup of dried prunes and apricots and $\frac{1}{2}$ cup of seeded raisins. She also includes 2 cups of sour red cherries. If the recipe makes 8 servings of fruit salad, what amounts would Chris use to make 4 servings?

   _____

6. Mary makes soup. Her recipe calls for $\frac{1}{2}$ teaspoon of salt and $\frac{1}{8}$ teaspoon of pepper. If she doubles the recipe, what would be the combined amount of salt and pepper that she would need? Give your answer two ways.

   _____

Subtract Fractions

CA Standards
KEY NS 3.2, NS 3.1

Subtract $\frac{1}{6}$ from $\frac{4}{6}$.

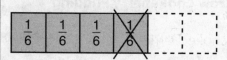

$\frac{4}{6} - \frac{1}{6} = \frac{3}{6}$

Next, compare $\frac{3}{6}$ and $\frac{1}{2}$.

$\frac{3}{6} = \frac{1}{2}$

Subtract. Use the picture to find the difference.

1.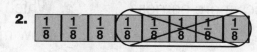

$\frac{6}{7} - \frac{3}{7} =$ _____

2.

$\frac{8}{8} - \frac{5}{8} =$ _____

3.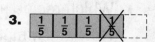

$\frac{4}{5} - \frac{1}{5} =$ _____

4. $\frac{2}{7} - \frac{1}{7} =$ _____

5. $\frac{6}{8} - \frac{4}{8} =$ _____

6. $\frac{9}{10} - \frac{2}{10} =$ _____

7. $\frac{7}{10} - \frac{5}{10} =$ _____

8. $\frac{8}{9} - \frac{4}{9} =$ _____

9. $\frac{4}{4} - \frac{2}{4} =$ _____

Spiral Review (Chapter 5, Lesson 2) **AF 1.5**

Find the missing number.

10. $4 \times 5 = 20$

$5 \times$ _____ $= 20$

11. $2 \times 6 = 12$

$6 \times$ _____ $= 12$

12. Which property of multiplication states that changing the order of the factors does not change the product?

_____

Homework and Problem Solving

153

Use with text pp. 352–353

Name _____ Date _____

Subtract Fractions

CA Standards
KEY NS 3.2, NS 3.1

The third-graders used the recipes below to make Native American desserts for Multicultural Day. Use the recipes to solve each problem.

Cherokee Blackberry Cobbler	
$\frac{1}{4}$ quart blackberries	$\frac{3}{6}$ cup honey
1 cup corn meal	$\frac{2}{16}$ cup butter
$\frac{1}{3}$ cup milk	1 egg slightly beaten

Crow Chokeberry Pudding	
$\frac{1}{2}$ quart chokecherries	$\frac{1}{6}$ cup honey
$\frac{1}{4}$ cup corn meal	4 cups water
$\frac{2}{6}$ cup milk	$\frac{1}{4}$ cup flour

Show your work.

1. Which recipe uses more berries? How much more?

_____

2. Which recipe uses more honey? How much more?

_____

3. Gilbert says that the pudding recipe uses $\frac{1}{3}$ cup more milk than the cobbler recipe. Do you agree? Explain why or why not.

_____

4. To find how much more corn meal is used in the cobbler, Nancy subtracted $\frac{4}{4} - \frac{1}{4} = \frac{3}{4}$. Did she get the correct result? Explain.

_____

_____

_____

5. The blackberry cobbler recipe makes 8 equal servings. Nina, Jack, and Cameron each ate $\frac{1}{4}$ of the servings. How many servings of cobbler were left over?

_____

6. How much more flour is used in the pudding recipe than butter in the cobbler recipe?

_____

Practice Adding and Subtracting Fractions

CA Standards
MR 1.2, **KEY** NS 3.2

Lena baked a cherry pie for dessert. She cut the pie into 6 equal pieces. Her sister ate $\frac{2}{6}$ of the pie and her mother ate $\frac{1}{6}$. How much pie is left?

Add the amounts Lena's sister and mother ate.

$\frac{2}{6} + \frac{1}{6} = \frac{3}{6}$

Remember that $1 = \frac{6}{6}$.

Subtract to get what part is left.

$\frac{6}{6} - \frac{3}{6} = \frac{3}{6}$ or $\frac{1}{2}$

One half of the pie is left.

Add or subtract.

1. $\frac{3}{11} + \frac{4}{11} =$ _____

2. $\frac{6}{7} - \frac{4}{7} =$ _____

3. $\frac{2}{5} + \frac{3}{5} =$ _____

Find the sum or difference. Then find a fraction in the box that is equivalent to the sum or difference.

$$\frac{1}{2}, \frac{2}{5}, \frac{5}{6}, \frac{1}{3}, \frac{2}{3}$$

4. $\frac{12}{12} - \frac{2}{12} =$ _____

5. $\frac{1}{4} + \frac{1}{4} =$ _____

6. $\frac{2}{9} + \frac{1}{9} =$ _____

Spiral Review (Chapter 5, Lesson 3) **KEY** NS 2.2

Find the product.

7. $2 \times 9 =$ _____

8. $8 \times 5 =$ _____

9. What are 2 different ways to multiply?

_____

_____

Practice Adding and Subtracting Fractions

CA Standards
MR 1.2, **KEY** NS 3.2

Solve each problem.

1. Jill's friends met at her house to go on a hike to the lake. They walked $\frac{1}{4}$ of the way and then rested. How much further do they have to go to reach the lake?

   _____

2. When they reached the lake, they took a swim. Jill swam $\frac{2}{3}$ across the lake and then swam back to shore. If she had continued, how much further would she have had to swim to reach the other side?

   _____

3. The hike back to Jill's house took an hour. They walked for $\frac{1}{2}$ hour and stopped for a water break. How much longer did they have to hike to get back to Jill's house? Write the answer in a fraction and in minutes.

   _____

4. When they arrived at Jill's, her mother served them a deli sandwich. She cut the sandwich into 12 sections. Jill and her 8 friends each ate 1 section. How much of the sandwich was left over? Answer with 2 equal fractions.

   _____

5. For dessert, Jill served her friends a chocolate cake. It was cut into 14 slices. Two of her friends don't eat chocolate. If everyone else had one slice, how much of the cake remained uneaten?

   _____

6. Peter's mother picked him up at Jill's house after they ate. Then she drove to the market to buy food. The market is $\frac{1}{3}$ of the way to Peter's house from Jill's. If the entire distance is 12 miles, how far is Peter's house from the market?

   _____

Hands On: Tenths and Hundredths

CA Standards
NS 3.0, NS 3.1

Model $\frac{2}{10}$.	Model $\frac{35}{100}$.
Shade 2 of the 10 equal parts.	Shade 35 of the 100 equal parts.

Model the fraction.

1. $\frac{6}{10}$

2. $\frac{8}{10}$

3. $\frac{3}{10}$

4. $\frac{11}{100}$

5. $\frac{34}{100}$

6. $\frac{8}{100}$

7. $\frac{80}{100}$

8. $\frac{52}{100}$

Spiral Review (Chapter 14, Lessons 2 and 3) **KEY NS 2.3, MR 2.4**

9. $36 \div 6 =$ _____

10. $54 \div 6 =$ _____

11. A desk has 49 crayons in it. An equal number of crayons are divided among 7 drawers in the desk. How many crayons are in each drawer? _____

Hands On: Tenths and Hundredths

Solve.

1. In a soccer game, Brett shot on goal 10 times. He made 1 goal. Write a fraction to show what part of all his shots resulted in a goal.

   _____

2. Janay also shot on goal 10 times. She made 3 goals. Write a fraction to show what part of all her shots resulted in a goal.

   _____

3. Tracy took a math test. He scored 90 points out of 100 possible points. Write a fraction to show what part of the possible points he earned.

   _____

4. Montez also took the math test. He scored 100 points out of 100 possible points. Write a fraction to show what part of the possible points he earned.

   _____

5. Erin's summer vacation lasted 100 days. She kept track of the number of rainy days. It rained on 30 days. Write a fraction and an equivalent fraction to show what part of all the days it rained.

   _____

6. Kira's winter break lasted 10 days. It snowed on 6 of those days. Write a fraction and an equivalent fraction to show what part of all the days it snowed.

   _____

Tenths

Write a fraction and a decimal for the shaded part.

- There are 10 parts in all.
- 9 parts or nine tenths are shaded.

$\frac{9}{10}$, 0.9

Write a fraction and a decimal for the shaded part.

1.

2.

3.

_____ _____ _____

Write as a decimal.

4. $\frac{1}{10}$

5. $\frac{6}{10}$

6. two tenths

7. five tenths

_____ _____ _____ _____

Write as a fraction.

8. 0.7

9. 0.8

10. three tenths

11. nine tenths

_____ _____ _____ _____

Spiral Review (Chapter 12, Lesson 4) **KEY** NS 2.3, MR 2.0

12. $14 \div 2 =$ _____

13. $35 \div 5 =$ _____

14. A fence has 25 boards. The boards are divided into 5 equal sections of the fence. How many boards are in each section? _____

Tenths

CA Standards
NS 3.4, NS 3.0

Six students each painted a section of the playground fence for a Fourth of July celebration. Each section had 10 fence posts. The table at the right shows how they chose to paint their fence sections. Use the table to solve each problem.

Playground Fence Painting			
Painter	Red Posts	White Posts	Blue Posts
Annie	7	2	1
Chun	1	3	6
Felipe	9	0	1
Hans	1	8	1
Matt	4	3	3
Nicole	3	5	2

1. Write a fraction and a decimal for the portion of the fence posts that Annie painted red.

_____

2. Who painted 9 fence posts red? What fraction and decimal names that part?

_____

3. Write a fraction and a decimal for the portion of fence posts that Matt painted red and white.

_____

4. Write a fraction and a decimal for the portion of fence posts that Nicole painted red and blue.

_____

5. Hans spent 6 minutes painting each of his fence posts. What fraction of his fence posts did he paint red and blue? How long did it take him to paint the red and blue posts?

_____

6. Write a fraction and a decimal for the portion of his fence posts that Felipe painted white.

_____

Use with text pp. 368–369

Hundredths

CA Standards
NS 3.4, NS 3.0

Write a fraction for the shaded part.	Write a decimal for the shaded part.	
• There are 100 parts in all.	Ninety-five hundredths are shaded.	
• 95 parts are shaded.	0.95	
$\frac{95}{100}$		

Find a fraction and a decimal for the shaded part.

1.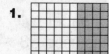

2.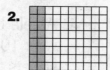

3.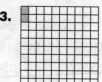

_____   _____   _____

Write as a decimal.

4. $\frac{23}{100}$

5. $\frac{85}{100}$

6. five hundredths

_____   _____   _____

7. $\frac{64}{100}$

8. $\frac{9}{100}$

9. seventy hundredths

_____   _____   _____

Spiral Review (Chapter 13, Lesson 4) **KEY NS 2.3, AF 1.2**

Find the quotient.

10. $45 \div 9 =$ _____

11. $63 \div 9 =$ _____

12. A store has 54 cans of paint. An equal number of cans are arranged on 9 shelves. How many cans are on each shelf? _____

Hundredths

Solve.

1. Amanda asked 100 students what item they liked best on the playground. Forty students chose the slide. What fraction and decimal represents the number of students who liked the slide the best?

2. Thirty-six students chose the swings as their favorite item on the playground. What fraction and decimal represents the number of students who liked the swings the best?

3. Caleb is reading a book that has 100 pages. He has read 62 pages. What decimal represents the number of pages he has left to read?

4. Akiela bought a pack of paper with 100 sheets. She has used 33 sheets. What fraction represents the number of pages she has left?

5. On one test, Chi answered 76 out of 100 questions correctly. On another test, he answered 7 out of 10 questions correctly. Write these scores as decimals and compare them.

6. In a survey, 8 out of 10 students said they would like more time for recess. Out of 100 teachers, 78 said they would not like to add more time for recess. Write these figures as decimals and compare them.

Hands On: Relate Fractions, Decimals, and Money

CA Standards
NS 3.4, NS 3.0

Complete the table. Use coins to help you.

	Coin(s)	Number of Cents	Fraction of a Dollar	Value as a Decimal
	1 quarter	A quarter is 25 cents. 25¢	A dollar is 100 cents. $\frac{25}{100}$	Write the fraction as a decimal. $0.25
1.	9 pennies			
2.	5 dimes			
3.	3 quarters			
4.	2 nickels			
5.	2 half-dollars			

Write the amount as the fraction of a dollar.

6. $0.76 = _____ of a dollar

7. $0.33 = _____ of a dollar

8. $0.04 = _____ of a dollar

9. $0.60 = _____ of a dollar

Spiral Review (Chapter 16, Lessons 2–4) **KEY** NS 3.2, NS 3.1

10. $\frac{3}{4} - \frac{1}{4} =$ _____

11. $\frac{1}{8} + \frac{6}{8} =$ _____

12. Simon used $\frac{2}{3}$ of a can of paint. How much paint is left in the can? _____

Hands On: Relate Fractions, Decimals, and Money

CA Standards
NS 3.4, NS 3.0

Solve. Use coins to help you.

1. Manny has $0.85. Jerry has $\frac{75}{100}$ of a dollar. Who has more money? Explain.

_____

_____

_____

2. Kim has $\frac{4}{10}$ of a dollar. Carla has $\frac{40}{100}$ of a dollar. Who has more money? Explain.

_____

_____

_____

3. Colin has 3 quarters. He says he has less than $\frac{8}{10}$ of a dollar. Is he correct? Explain.

_____

_____

4. Laura has $\frac{52}{100}$ of a dollar. She wants to buy two pencils that cost 25¢ each. Does she have enough money? Explain.

_____

_____

5. Megan has $\frac{1}{4}$ of a dollar. She wants to buy a folder that costs $0.10 and a pen that costs 35¢. Does she have enough money? Explain.

_____

_____

6. If Megan had $\frac{3}{4}$ of a dollar, how many folders could she buy and also buy a pen? Explain.

_____

_____

_____

Reasonable Answers

CA Standards
MR 3.1, NS 3.4

Karl has saved $2.90. He wishes to use $1.50 to buy a birthday present for his sister. How much money will Karl have left after buying the present? $2.40

Step ❶ First, ask yourself if the answer is reasonable. This problem requires subtraction to find an amount of money. It makes sense that Karl has less money than he started with, so the answer is reasonable.

Step ❷ Now solve the problem to see if the answer is correct.
$2.90 − $1.50 = $1.40

Solution: The answer is reasonable but incorrect.

Tell whether the answer is reasonable. Then solve the problem and tell if the answer is correct.

1. There is 0.6 of a mile between Devon's house and Elyssa's house. Both Devon and Elyssa walk toward the other person's house and meet at the halfway point. How far does each person walk? Devon answers: **0.3 of a mile**

_____

2. Rachel's father slices 4 oranges into quarters. Rachel puts 8 orange quarters in the refrigerator. What fraction represents the amount of the 4 oranges that are left? Rachel answers: $\frac{1}{4}$

_____

Spiral Review (Chapter 16, Lessons 2–4) **KEY NS 3.2, NS 3.1**

Add or subtract.

3. $\frac{2}{3} + \frac{2}{3} =$ _____

4. $\frac{4}{9} - \frac{3}{9} =$ _____

5. How is problem 4 similar to a problem in which you are subtracting whole numbers?

_____

_____

Reasonable Answers

Tell whether the answer is reasonable. Then solve the problem and tell if the answer is correct.

1. Jermaine has 30 cents. He finds 25 cents on the sidewalk. How much money does he have now? He answers: **55 cents**

_____

_____

_____

2. Jody has 45 cents. Her brother has 35 cents. How much money do they have in all? She answers: **70 cents**

_____

_____

_____

3. Kesara earns $0.50 an hour being a "mother's helper." During one week she worked as a mother's helper for 5 hours. How much money did Kesara earn that week? She answers: **$2.00**

_____

_____

_____

4. Jon has 85 cents. He buys a pocket notebook for 40 cents. How much money does he have left? He answers: **45 cents**

_____

_____

_____

5. Rafael has saved 80 cents. He earns 25 cents more from his grandfather. How much money does he have now? He answers: **$1.50**

_____

_____

6. A fence has 60 pickets. A dozen of these pickets need to be replaced. How many pickets do not need to be replaced? Answer: **72**

_____

_____

Hands On: Add and Subtract Money Amounts

CA Standards
KEY NS 3.3, MR 2.0

Becca bought a bag of erasers and a box of crayons for school. How much did she spend in all?

Item	Cost
Bag of erasers	$1.38
Pack of markers	$4.50
Box of crayons	$2.56
Pack of folders	$1.25

- Count out $1.38 and $2.56 in dollars, dimes, and pennies. Group the dollars, dimes, and pennies.

Dollars   Dimes   Pennies

- Add the pennies. Regroup 10 pennies as 1 dime.

Dollars   Dimes   Pennies
   3   9   4

- Add the dimes. You don't need to regroup.
- Add the dollars. Write the total amount.

Solution: She spent $3.94.

Use the table above and play money to solve the problems.

1. Rosa bought a pack of folders and a box of crayons. How much did she spend in all?

_____

2. What is the total cost of 2 bags of erasers?

_____

Spiral Review   (Chapter 11, Lesson 2) **MG 2.5, MG 2.6**

For 3–4, name the solid figure.

3.

4.

5. Which solid figure looks like a cereal box?

_____   _____   _____

Name _____ Date _____

Hands On: Add and Subtract Money Amounts

Use a table and play money to solve each problem. Item Prices: postcard ($1.13), key chain ($3.87), Park Ranger patch ($5.33), and stuffed animal ($8.79).

1. Jaime bought a postcard and a key chain. How much did he spend in all?

   _____

2. Darla bought a Park Ranger patch and key chain. How much did she spend in all?

   _____

3. Abraham wanted to buy a Park Ranger patch. He had 4 dollar bills and 11 dimes, but he needed to borrow 23¢. How much money did Abraham have before borrowing 23¢?

   _____

4. Who (Jaime, Darla, or Abraham) could have paid for his or her purchases with 3 bills and 20 coins? How many dollar bills do the coins equal?

   _____

5. Darla returned the key chain and Park Ranger patch, and bought a stuffed animal and a postcard instead. How much money did she spend on the stuffed animal and postcard? How much more money did she spend on her new purchases than on the key chain and patch?

   _____

6. Darla's mother had only given Darla $10.00. Darla also had some money of her own. She wanted to buy one more postcard. She bought the stuffed animal and postcard with her mother's money. Would she need to spend any of her own money for the postcard? If so, how much? If not, how much would she have left?

   _____

Add Money Amounts

Lok bought a pack of postcards for $2.60 and some stamps for
$3.90. How much did he spend in all?

• Write the numbers with the decimal points lined up.

• Add the hundredths.
• Add the tenths. Regroup.
• Add the ones.

Solution: He spent $6.50.

```
     1
  $2.60
 +3.90
  $6.50
```

Add.

1. $3.52 + $2.75 =

_____

2. $2.56 + $1.43 =

_____

3. $53.07 + $16.27 =

_____

4. $25.93 + $69.68 =

_____

5. $3.57 + $4.25 =

_____

6. $56.79 + $13.88 =

_____

7. $3.48 + $2.24 + $5.32 =

_____

8. $5.31 + $1.61 + $4.67 =

_____

9. $1.48 + $4.52 + $8.06 =

_____

Spiral Review (Chapter 13, Lesson 2) **KEY** NS 2.3, NS 2.0

10. 36 ÷ 4 = _____

11. 24 ÷ 3 = _____

12. Mrs. Dade bought 12 bagels for the 4 members of her family.
How many bagels can each person have?

_____

Name _____ Date _____

Add Money Amounts

CA Standard
KEY NS 3.3

Add to solve each problem.

1. Frankie bought two mechanical pencils. Each pencil cost $3.87. What was the total the cost for the two pencils?

   _____

2. Annabella bought two hair ribbons. Each cost $5.28. What was the total cost for the two hair ribbons?

   _____

3. Sue bought a box of juice that cost $2.62, a sandwich that cost $5.68, and an orange that cost $0.75. What was the total cost of the three items?

   _____

4. Luis bought new shoelaces for $2.85, sweatbands for his wrists for $3.88, and a bottle of sports drink for $1.75. What was the total cost for the three items?

   _____

5. Brandon bought one more pair of sweatbands than Luis. Each pair of sweatbands cost $3.88. He also bought one more bottle of sports drink than Luis, each costing $1.75, and a granola bar, costing $0.98. What was the total cost of Brandon's purchase?

   _____

6. Katrina and her mother went to the sports store to buy tennis supplies. Her mother bought Katrina one tennis outfit for $28.59. She also bought 5 pairs of tennis socks. One pair cost $2.85, another cost $3.55, and the remaining three pairs were packaged together at 3 for $6.00. How much did they spend at the sports store?

   _____

Subtract Money Amounts

Find $5.00 − $2.32.

- There are no hundredths or tenths in $5.00 to subtract from, so regroup the ones.
- Regroup the tenths and hundredths.
- Subtract.

Solution: $2.68

$$\begin{array}{r} \overset{9}{\underset{4\ \cancel{10}\ 10}{}} \\ \$\cancel{5}.\cancel{0}\cancel{0} \\ -2.32 \\ \hline \end{array}$$

Subtract. Check by adding.

1. $5.72 − $2.41 = _____

2. $8.69 − $3.97 = _____

3. $4.15 − $2.37 = _____

4. $8.20 − $2.86 = _____

5. $75.15 − $10.61 = _____

6. $54.28 − $38.74 = _____

7. $97.00 − $59.54 = _____

8. $60.00 − $19.47 = _____

9. $76.53 − $34.54 = _____

Spiral Review (Chapter 15, Lesson 4) **KEY NS 3.1**

10. Write an equivalent fraction for $\frac{3}{4}$. _____

11. Write an equivalent fraction for $\frac{2}{5}$. _____

12. Mason lives $\frac{5}{10}$ mile from school. Tyler lives $\frac{4}{8}$ mile from school. Do they live the same distance from school? Explain.

_____

Subtract Money Amounts

CA Standards
KEY NS 3.3, MR 3.2

Subtract to solve the problems. Check by adding.

1. Aidan has $5.00 to buy a can of tennis balls that cost $3.79. How much change should he get back?

   _____

   _____

2. Sylvia has $10.00 to buy a hairbrush that cost $6.88. How much change should she get back?

   _____

   _____

3. Elvis bought a CD for $15.99. He paid with $13.00 and 30 dimes. How much change did Elvis get back?

   _____

   _____

4. Tawny has 4 one-dollar bills, 20 dimes, and 100 pennies. She bought a knit cap, which cost $6.26. How much change did Tawny get back?

   _____

   _____

5. Tomas and Davis went to the local craft store to buy model kits. Together the boys had $25.00 to spend. Tomas' model race-car kit cost $12.59. Davis' model airplane kit cost $9.65. The glue cost $2.25. How much change did the boys receive?

   _____

   _____

6. Rosie and Shoshana went skating. They had $20.00 each to spend. The entrance fee was $7.00. The skate rental fee depended on the type of skates rented. Speed skates cost $11.00. Inline skates cost $10.50. Rosie rented speed skates, and Shoshana rented inline skates. After the entrance fee and skate rental, how much change did each girl receive?

   _____

   _____

Name _____ Date _____

Function Tables and Money

CA Standards
KEY AF 2.1, AF 2.0

Find the function rule and complete the function table.

Deana sells movie tickets. She made this function table to show the cost of multiple tickets. How much would 4 tickets cost?

Input (Number of Tickets)	Output (Total Cost)
1	$8.00
2	$16.00
3	$24.00

- Find the relationship between the input and the output.

- Use this relationship to solve the problem.

The rule is multiply by $8.00.

Solution: Four tickets would cost $32.00.

$4 \times \$8 = \$32$

1.

Input	Output
$1.50	
$2.75	$5.75
$3.25	
$4.50	$7.50

Rule: _____

2.

Input	Output
3	
4	$20.00
5	
6	$30.00

Rule: _____

3.

Input	Output
$5.45	
$9.75	$5.75
$8.14	
$11.50	$7.50

Rule: _____

4.

Input	Output
$3.00	
$5.00	$3.50
$7.00	
$9.00	$7.50

Rule: _____

Spiral Review (Chapter 17, Lessons 2–3) NS 3.0, NS 3.4

Solve.

5. Write 0.2 as a fraction. _____

6. Write $\frac{71}{100}$ as a decimal. _____

7. Out of 100 students, 52 ride a bus to school. What decimal represents the number of students who ride a bus to school? _____

Function Tables and Money

CA Standards
KEY AF 2.1, AF 2.0

Use the function tables to solve the problems.

Input (Original Price of Store Items)	Output (Sale Price)
$7.00	
$3.86	$1.61
$9.89	
$14.21	$11.96

Input (Number of Pies Sold)	Output (Cost)
1	$12.65
2	
3	$37.95
4	

1. What is the rule for Table 1? What are the missing output entries in Table 1?

_____

_____

_____

2. What is the rule for Table 2? What are the missing output entries in Table 2?

_____

_____

_____

3. If a fifth item in the Table 1 originally cost $8.42, what would the output number be?

_____

_____

4. Following the same rule set in Table 2, what would the output number be if 7 pies were sold?

_____

_____

5. Suppose the output prices of the store items, including the new item added in Problem 3, were $2.25 greater than the input prices. Would that change the rule? What would the new output numbers be?

_____

_____

_____

_____

6. Suppose the output number for three pies sold in Table 2 was $42.00. How would that change the rule, and what would the new output numbers be for Table 2?

_____

_____

_____

_____

Write a Number Sentence

CA Standards
MR 2.4, KEY AF 1.1

Andrew gives a cashier $5 to pay for a carton of milk. The milk costs $1.89. How much change will Andrew get back?

Step 1 Identify the information the problem gives. The milk costs $1.89. Andrew gives the cashier $5.00.

Step 2 Write a number sentence to solve the problem. Decide which operation to use.

$5.00 - $1.89 =

Step 3 Subtract.

$5.00 - $1.89 = $3.11

Solution: Andrew will get back $3.11.

Write a number sentence to solve each problem. Explain why your answer makes sense.

1. Wanda saves $7.25. She wishes to spend $3.65 on a set of special markers. If she buys the markers, how much money will she have left?

_____

2. Ella is putting together money she has saved in three small banks in her bedroom. One bank contains $3.12. Another bank has $1.79 in it. The third bank contains $2.26. How much money has Ella saved in all?

_____

_____

Spiral Review (Chapter 9, Lessons 2 and 4) **KEY** MG 2.1, **KEY** MG 2.2

Tell whether the figure is a polygon. If it is, write its name.

3.   4.

_____   _____

5. Is a triangle a polygon? Explain why or why not.

_____

_____

_____

Write a Number Sentence

Write a number sentence to solve each problem.

1. Ms. Bearce had $4.30 in her pocket. She bought a magazine for $3.00. How much money did she have left?

_____

_____

2. Tom found $2.75 in the pocket of a jacket he had not worn for nearly a year. He added this money to the $5.20 he had saved in his bank. How much money did Tom have in all?

_____

_____

3. Julia was given a gift of $2.50. She added this money to the $7.18 she had saved. How much money did she have in all?

_____

_____

4. Rachel bought a book and a magazine and spent a total of $9.38. The price of the magazine was $2.95. What was the price of the book?

_____

_____

5. Kelsey bought milk, bread, and butter at a store and spent a total of $9.63. She spent $3.99 on milk and $2.69 on bread. What was the price of the butter?

_____

_____

6. Mr. Skillin used a 20-dollar bill and a 10-dollar bill to pay for a new portable radio. The cashier gave him $9.62 back in change. How much did the radio cost?

_____

_____

Hands On: Multiplication Patterns with 10, 100, and 1,000

CA Standards
KEY NS 2.4, MR 1.1

What is the product of $5 \times 1,000$?

Notice the pattern with $5 \times 1 = 5$ and $5 \times 10 = 50$ and $5 \times 100 = 500$.

Solution: The product $5 \times 1,000$ equals 5,000.

Fill in the missing number sentences in the table.

	Multiply by 1	Multiply by 10	Multiply by 100	Multiply by 1,000
1.	$4 \times 1 = 4$		$4 \times 100 = 400$	
2.		$7 \times 10 = 70$		
3.			$8 \times 100 = 800$	
4.				$3 \times 1,000 = 3,000$
5.	$2 \times 1 = 2$			

Spiral Review (Chapters 15, Lesson 5 and Chapter 16, Lessons 1,3,4)
MR 2.3, NS 3.1, **KEY** NS 3.2

Subtract. Use fraction tiles to help.

6. $\frac{5}{6} - \frac{2}{6}$

7. $\frac{8}{9} - \frac{4}{9}$

8. Matt and Jamie are sharing a pizza. If Matt eats $\frac{1}{4}$ of the pizza and Jamie eats $\frac{3}{8}$ of the pizza, who eats more?

_____

Hands On: Multiplication Patterns with 10, 100, and 1,000

CA Standards
KEY NS 2.4, MR 1.1

Use a basic fact and patterns to find the product.

1. Rebecca has 4 boxes of 20 cookies. She wants to know the total number of cookies. Which basic fact must she know to compute the total? What is the total?

_____

_____

2. Jeremy is at a theater. There are 5 rows with 20 seats in each row. He knows that $5 \times 2 = 10$. How can he use this fact to find the total number of seats in the theater?

_____

_____

_____

3. Marnie needs 4,000 flowers for a wedding. She has 6 boxes of 400 flowers. How many more flowers does she need?

_____

4. Dave has 5 albums with 70 photos in each album. Jake has 8 albums with 90 photos in each album. How many photos do Dave and Jake have altogether?

_____

5. Seth bikes 3 miles in 10 minutes and 30 miles in 100 minutes. Use a pattern to find out how many miles Seth bikes in 1,000 minutes? Is this realistic?

_____

_____

6. In 10 jumps on her pogo stick, Basia covered a distance of 20 feet. In 100 jumps, she went 200 feet. In 1,000 jumps, she went 2,000 feet. What distance does Basia cover with each jump on her pogo stick?

_____

Multipy with Multiples of 10, 100, or 1,000

CA Standards
KEY NS 2.4, MR 1.1

Use a basic fact and pattern to find the product.

		Solution:
$2 \times 8 =$ _____	Look for a pattern of zeros.	$2 \times 8 = 16$
$2 \times 80 =$ _____		$2 \times 8\underline{0} = 16\underline{0}$
$2 \times 800 =$ _____		$2 \times 8\underline{00} = 1,6\underline{00}$
$2 \times 8,000 =$ _____		$2 \times 8,\underline{000} = 16,\underline{000}$

1. $3 \times 3 =$ _____

$3 \times 30 =$ _____

$3 \times 300 =$ _____

$3 \times 3,000 =$ _____

2. $6 \times 3 =$ _____

$6 \times 30 =$ _____

$6 \times 300 =$ _____

$6 \times 3,000 =$ _____

3. $4 \times 8 =$ _____

$4 \times 80 =$ _____

$4 \times 800 =$ _____

$4 \times 8,000 =$ _____

4. 7×80

_____

5. 3×900

_____

6. $3 \times 2,000$

_____

7. 4×50

_____

8. 3×500

_____

9. 3×400

_____

10. 3×90

_____

11. 8×700

_____

Spiral Review (Chapter 16, Lessons 1–4) MR 2.3, NS 3.1, **KEY** NS 3.2

Find the sum.

12. $\dfrac{3}{5} + \dfrac{1}{5}$

13. $\dfrac{2}{9} + \dfrac{6}{9}$

14. Enzo and Eric are sharing a pie. If Enzo eats $\dfrac{1}{3}$ of the pie and Eric eats $\dfrac{1}{5}$ of the pie, is there more than $\dfrac{1}{2}$ of the pie remaining? _____

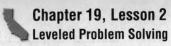
Multiply with Multiples of 10, 100, and 1,000

CA Standards
KEY NS 2.4, MR 1.1

Use a basic fact and patterns to find the product.

1. Toy City just recevied a shipment of 9 boxes of yo-yos. Each box holds 600 yo-yos. How many yo-yos are in the shipment altogether? What basic fact did you use to find your product?

_____

_____

2. Each yo-yo costs $3. Toy City sold 40 yo-yos in June and 400 yo-yos in July. What was the total value of those yo-yo sales? What basic fact did you use to find your answer?

_____

_____

3. Toy City ordered 6 boxes of jump ropes. Each box has 700 jump ropes. The store needs 5,000 jump ropes in stock for a big sale. How many more jump ropes should be ordered? How do you know?

_____

_____

4. Toy City has 8 boxes of pogo sticks in its warehouse. Each box has 50 pogo sticks. The store manager says that there are 4,000 pogo sticks in the warehouse. What's wrong?

_____

_____

5. In March, Toy City sold 40 basketballs at $9 each and 50 yo-yos at $3 each. In April, Toy City sold 50 basketballs and 30 yo-yos. What is the difference of the total value of sales between March and April?

_____

6. Toy City can sell 300 yo-yos at $3 each. If yo-yos go on sale for $2 each, Toy City predicts it will sell 700 yo-yos. How much more money does Toy City make when it sells the yo-yos for the sale price?

_____

Estimate Products

CA Standard
KEY MR 2.5

Estimate the product.

Example

485
× 4

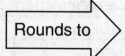
Rounds to

500
× 4
2,000

Solution: So, 4 × 485 is about 2,000

1.	2.	3.	4.	5.
38 × 4	810 × 6	875 × 6	64 × 4	43 × 7

6. 72 × 5 _____   7. 8 × 38 _____   8. 5 × 913 _____   9. 4 × 689 _____   10. 9 × 61 _____

Compare. Write >, <, or = for each ◯.

11. 2 × 58 ◯ 2 × 48

12. 3 × 800 ◯ 4 × 600

13. 11 × 33 ◯ 333 × 11

14. 281 × 4 ◯ 412 × 4

Spiral Review (Chapter 16, Lessons 1, 3, 4) **KEY** NS 3.2

Find the value of ▢ **.**

15. $\frac{4}{9} + \frac{\boxed{}}{9} = \frac{8}{9}$

16. $\frac{\boxed{}}{8} - \frac{3}{8} = \frac{2}{8}$

17. Ruby and Marielle are working on a project. If Ruby finishes $\frac{4}{8}$ of the project and Marielle finishes $\frac{3}{8}$, how much of the project is left?

_____

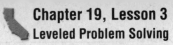
Estimate Products

CA Standard
MR 2.5

The table below shows the amounts of some foods the
average American eats each year. Estimate the product.
Round the larger factor to its greatest place.

1. About how much chocolate does an
average American eat in 5 years?

_____

2. About how much fish does an average
American eat in 3 years?

_____

3. Which food makes up the largest part
of most Americans' diets? About how
much of that food does the average
American eat in 4 years?

_____

_____

4. In 2 years, about how much more
fruit than sugar does the average
American eat?

_____

_____

5. Mr. and Mrs. Johnson have three
daughters and two sons. If all the
Johnsons eat as many potatoes as
the average American, about how
much potatoes will the entire family
eat this year?

_____

Average American Yearly Diet	
Food	**Amount**
Bread	46 pounds
Chocolate	13 pounds
Dairy Products	582 pounds
Fish	51 pounds
Fruit	261 pounds
Meat	270 pounds
Potatoes	141 pounds
Sugar	67 pounds
Vegetables	267 pounds

6. Max eats 5 times as many pounds
of chocolate as the average
American and twice the amount of
potatoes. About how many more
pounds of chocolate and potatoes
does Max eat than the average
American?

_____

_____

Hands On:
Multiply Two-Digit Numbers

CA Standards
KEY NS 2.4, MR 2.3

**Use base-ten blocks to multiply a 1-digit number
by a 2-digit number.**

21 × 3 = _____

Step 1 Use base-ten blocks to show 3 groups of 21.

Step 2 Count the tens blocks. _____

Count the ones blocks. _____

Solution: Record your answer. 21 × 3 = _____

Use base-ten blocks to help you find the product.

1. 2 × 14 = _____

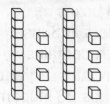

2. 3 × 32 = _____

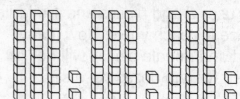

3. 3 × 33 = _____

4. 4 × 11 = _____

5. 5 × 10 = _____

6. 2 × 23 = _____

7. 3 × 22 = _____

8. 4 × 21 = _____

Spiral Review (Chapter 17, Lesson 4) **NS 3.4, NS 3.0**

Write the amount as a fraction of a dollar.

9. $0.25 _____

10. $0.50 _____

11. If an item costs $\frac{3}{4}$ of a dollar, how much does it cost? _____

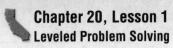
Hands On:
Multiply Two-Digit Numbers

Multiply.

1. A box holds 10 yo-yos. How many yo-yos are in 4 boxes?

_____

2. Mr. Tomkins is making yo-yos. He can make 12 yo-yos an hour. How many yo-yos can he make in 3 hours?

_____

3. He uses 2 feet of string in each small yo-yo. How much string will he use in 14 small yo-yos?

_____

4. He uses 4 feet of string in each jumbo yo-yo. If he makes a dozen jumbo yo-yos, how much string will he use?

_____

5. He uses 2 end pieces and 1 middle piece for each yo-yo. How many end and middle pieces will he need for two dozen yo-yos?

_____

6. Mr. Tomkins gave 3 boxes of yo-yos to third graders at Sunset Elementary. Each box contains 20 yo-yos. There are 2 third-grade classes. Each class has 23 students. Are there enough yo-yos to give one to each student? Explain your answer.

_____

Multiply 2-Digit Numbers

CA Standard
KEY NS 2.4

Multiply.

A tricycle has 3 tires. How many tires are on 23 tricycles?
Find 23 × 3.

Step ① Multiply the ones. 3 × 3 ones = 9 ones

Step ② Multiply the tens. 3 × 2 tens = 6 tens

Solution: There are 69 tires on 23 tricycles.

1. 12
    × 4

2. 31
    × 3

3. 11
    × 5

4. 22
    × 4

5. 34
    × 2

6. 21
    × 4

Spiral Review (Chapter 17, Lesson 4) **NS 3.4, NS 3.0**

Write <, >, or =.

7. 50 ¢ _____ $\frac{1}{2}$ of a dollar

8. 25 ¢ _____ $\frac{3}{10}$ of a dollar

9. How many pennies are there in 10 ¢? _____

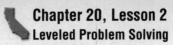
Multiply 2-Digit Numbers

CA Standard
KEY NS 2.4

Solve the problems below.

1. A dolly buggy has 4 tires. How many tires are on 12 buggies?

_____

2. A unicycle has 1 tire. How many tires are on 36 unicycles?

_____

3. New cars are sold with 4 tires plus a spare tire. How many tires are needed for 10 new cars?

_____

4. How many tires are on 32 tricycles?

_____

5. There are 2 tires on the front of a school bus. There are 4 tires on the back of a school bus. How many tires are on 10 school buses?

_____

6. A 16-wheeler truck has 16 tires. The cab of a 16-wheeler has 6 tires. The trailer has 10. How many tires are on 11 truck cabs?

_____

Hands On: Regroup in Multiplication

CA Standards
KEY NS 2.4, MR 2.1

Use base-ten blocks to help you find the product. Then estimate to check your answer.

Teri's grandfather walks for 15 minutes every day. How much time does he spend walking every week?

Step 1 Use base-ten blocks to show 7 groups of 15.

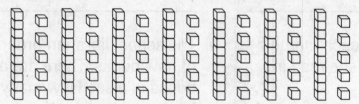

Step 2 Regroup when you have 10 or more ones blocks.

Step 3 Estimate to check your answer.

Solution: Teri's grandfather spends 105 minutes walking every week.

1. $3 \times 15 =$ _____

2. $19 \times 2 =$ _____

3. $26 \times 3 =$ _____

4. $3 \times 18 =$ _____

5. $2 \times 15 =$ _____

6. $47 \times 2 =$ _____

7. $35 \times 2 =$ _____

8. $17 \times 4 =$ _____

9. $4 \times 23 =$ _____

Spiral Review (Chapter 19, Lesson 3) **MR 2.5**

Estimate to find the product.

10. 76×2 _____

11. 322×3 _____

12. A store clerk unpacked 82 cartons of light bulbs. Each carton held 4 light bulbs. About how many light bulbs

were in the cartons? _____

Hands On: Regroup in Multiplication

CA Standards
KEY NS 2.4, MR 2.1

Solve each problem. Use base-ten blocks to help you.

1. Carmen can type 15 pages a day. How many pages can she type in 5 days?

_____

2. Kevin reads 16 pages of a book every hour. How many pages will he read in 3 hours?

_____

3. Eileen reads 3 books each month. How many books will she read in one year?

_____

4. The school librarian ordered 6 sets of new books. There are a dozen books in a set. How many new books did the librarian order?

_____

5. Oma read 16 pages an hour for 4 hours. Pat read 18 pages for 3 hours. Write a mathematical sentence that tells who read more pages.

_____

6. To find 4 × 29, Clarence multiplied 4 × 20. Then he multiplied 4 × 9. Then he added his two products. Do you think his method worked? Explain.

_____

Regroup in Multiplication

Find the product.

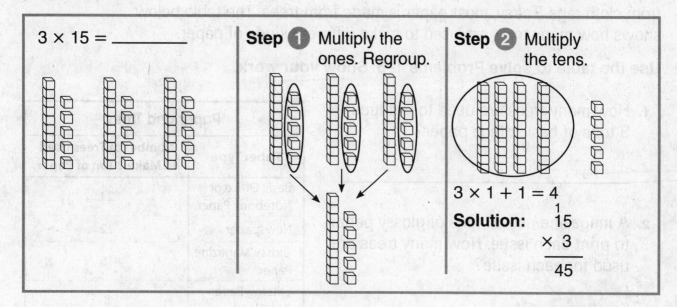

$3 \times 15 =$ _____	**Step 1** Multiply the ones. Regroup.	**Step 2** Multiply the tens.
		$3 \times 1 + 1 = 4$
		Solution: $\begin{array}{r} 1 \\ 15 \\ \times\ 3 \\ \hline 45 \end{array}$

1. $2 \times 14 =$ _____   **2.** $4 \times 15 =$ _____   **3.** $3 \times 17 =$ _____

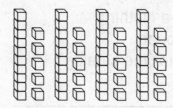

4. $\begin{array}{r} 16 \\ \times\ 3 \\ \hline \end{array}$

5. $\begin{array}{r} 13 \\ \times\ 7 \\ \hline \end{array}$

6. $5 \times 18 =$ _____

7. $2 \times 15 =$ _____

8. $3 \times 52 =$ _____

Spiral Review   (Chapter 19, Lesson 3) **MR 2.5**

Estimate the product.

9. $6 \times 28 =$ _____

10. $3 \times 432 =$ _____

11. Bryan's father can read 48 pages in an hour. About how many pages can he read in 6 hours? _____

Regroup in Multiplication

Paper was invented in China in A.D. 105. At that time, paper was made from cloth rags. Today, most paper is made from trees. The table below shows how many trees are used to make different kinds of paper.

Use the table to solve Problems 1–6. Show your work.

1. How many trees are used to produce 3 tons of basic office paper?

_____

2. A magazine uses 6 tons of glossy paper to print each issue. How many trees are used for each issue?

_____

Paper and Trees	
Paper Type	Number of Trees Used to Make 1 Ton of Paper
Basic Office or Notebook Paper	24
Newspaper	12
Glossy Magazine Paper	15
Catalog Paper (No Gloss)	8

3. To print its spring catalog, a clothing company uses 91 tons of paper. How many trees are used for the catalog?

_____

4. Which uses more trees: 5 tons of notebook paper or 10 tons of catalog paper?

_____

5. Which uses fewer trees: 8 tons of newspaper or 8 tons of magazine paper? Write a mathematical sentence that tells the answer.

_____

6. Which type of paper uses 3 times as many trees as catalog paper?

_____

Use a Simpler Problem

CA Standards
MR 2.2, **KEY** NS 2.4

Solve. Explain why your answer makes sense.

One photo album fits 4 photographs on each page. This album contains 55 pages. Another photo album fits 3 photographs on each of its 70 pages. If Mr. and Mrs. Jagger fill both albums, how many photographs will they use in all?

Step ❶ Choose easier numbers. What if the first album contained 5 pages, and the second album contained 7 pages?
Multiply.
4 × 5 = 20
3 × 7 = 21
Add.
20 + 21 = 41

Step ❷ Solve the problem using the original numbers.
Multiply.
4 × 55 = 220
3 × 70 = 210
Add.
220 + 210 = 430

Solution: In all, Mr. and Mrs. Jagger will use 430 photographs.

1. A restaurant uses 14 dozen eggs each day. If the restaurant is open 7 days each week, how many eggs will they use in 4 weeks? _____

2. Mrs. Stahl delivers mail. She walks a route of 6 miles each day. She delivers mail on this route 347 days during the course of a year. How many miles does she walk to deliver mail in all? _____

Spiral Review (Chapter 18, Lesson 4) **KEY AF 2.1**

Find the function rule and complete the function table.
Rule: _____

	Input	Output
3.	$3.55	
	$4.88	$3.48
4.	$6.21	
	$7.54	$6.14

5. What would the output be if the input was $10.20? _____

Name _____ Date _____

Use a Simpler Problem

CA Standards
MR 2.2, **KEY** NS 2.4

Solve. Explain why your answer makes sense.

1. Michelle rides the bus to school and home again 3 days each week. Michelle attends school for 35 weeks. How many school bus rides does she take in all?

_____

2. There are 17 girls and 8 boys sitting in the seats on the left side of a school bus. There are 19 boys and 9 girls sitting in the seats on the right side of the bus. How many students are seated on the bus in all?

_____

3. A school bus has 2 rows of seats. Each row contains 11 seats. Each seat holds 3 children. If each seat has 1 empty space, how many children are seated on the bus?

_____

4. A school bus travels 12 miles each day. The bus travels the same route Monday through Friday. But on every Saturday the bus travels just 3 miles. How far has the bus traveled after 4 weeks?

_____

5. A school bus has 42 panes of glass in its passenger windows. There are 5 of these school buses in a parking lot. If both sides of every window must be cleaned, how many panes of glass will be cleaned in all?

_____

6. The engine of a school bus runs for 63 minutes each weekday morning and each weekday afternoon. How long does the engine run during the course of one school week?

_____

Hands On: Multiply Greater Numbers

CA Standard
KEY NS 2.4

Find 2 × 155.

Step **1** Show 2 groups of 155.

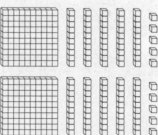

Step **2** Regroup the ones. Then regroup the tens. Now there are 3 hundreds blocks, and 1 tens block.

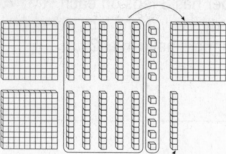

Solution: 2 × 155 = 310.

Use base-ten blocks to help you find the product.

1. 5 × 126 = _____   2. 2 × 351 = _____   3. 3 × 137 = _____

4. 4 × 123 = _____   5. 3 × 248 = _____   6. 2 × 447 = _____

Spiral Review (Chapter 16, Lessons 2, 3) **KEY** NS 3.2

Solve.

7. $\frac{3}{6} + \frac{2}{6} =$ _____   8. $\frac{3}{10} + \frac{4}{10} =$ _____

9. Tonya, Enrique, and Amy shared an 8-piece pizza. Tonya ate $\frac{2}{8}$. Enrique ate $\frac{3}{8}$. Amy ate $\frac{1}{8}$. How much of the pizza is left?

_____

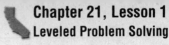
Hands On: Multiply Greater Numbers

CA Standard
KEY NS 2.4

Find the product.

1. Most insects have 3 body parts. How many body parts do 224 insects have in all?

   _____

2. Beetles have 4 wings. How many wings do 152 beetles have in all?

   _____

3. A grasshopper has 3 legs on each side of its body. How many legs do 135 grasshoppers have in all?

   _____

4. A colony of honeybees can make 400 pounds of honey in a year. How much honey could 5 colonies of honeybees make in a year?

   _____

5. Most insects have 3 pairs of mouthparts. How many mouthparts do 337 insects have in all?

   _____

6. Insects have 1 pair of antennae and 2 pairs of wings. Write a mathematical sentence that compares the number of antennae and the number of wings of 236 insects.

   _____

Multiply a 3-Digit Number
by a 1-Digit Number

CA Standards
KEY NS 2.4, MR 2.1

Find the product of 4 × 116.

Step ① Multiply the ones.	**Step ② Multiply the tens and add the 2 regrouped tens.**	**Step ③ Multiply the hundreds.**
$4 \times 6 = 24$. Regroup 24 ones as 2 tens 4 ones.	$4 \times 1 + 2 = 6$.	$4 \times 1 = 4$.
$\begin{array}{r} \overset{2}{116} \\ \times\ \ 4 \\ \hline 4 \end{array}$	$\begin{array}{r} \overset{2}{116} \\ \times\ \ 4 \\ \hline 64 \end{array}$	$\begin{array}{r} \overset{2}{116} \\ \times\ \ 4 \\ \hline 464 \end{array}$

Find the product. Estimate to see if your answer is reasonable.

1. $\begin{array}{r} 311 \\ \times\ \ 3 \\ \hline \end{array}$

2. $\begin{array}{r} 162 \\ \times\ \ 4 \\ \hline \end{array}$

3. $\begin{array}{r} 308 \\ \times\ \ 2 \\ \hline \end{array}$

4. $\begin{array}{r} 225 \\ \times\ \ 2 \\ \hline \end{array}$

5. $\begin{array}{r} 318 \\ \times\ \ 3 \\ \hline \end{array}$

6. $\begin{array}{r} 116 \\ \times\ \ 5 \\ \hline \end{array}$

7. $\begin{array}{r} 300 \\ \times\ \ 3 \\ \hline \end{array}$

8. $\begin{array}{r} 162 \\ \times\ \ 4 \\ \hline \end{array}$

9. $\begin{array}{r} 126 \\ \times\ \ 3 \\ \hline \end{array}$

10. $\begin{array}{r} 121 \\ \times\ \ 6 \\ \hline \end{array}$

Spiral Review (Chapter 16, Lesson 3) **KEY NS 3.2**

Find the difference.

11. $\dfrac{7}{8} - \dfrac{2}{8} =$ _____

12. $\dfrac{4}{5} - \dfrac{1}{5} =$ _____

13. Jason and Carlo shared a pizza. Jason ate $\dfrac{2}{6}$ of the pizza. Carlo ate $\dfrac{1}{6}$ of the pizza. How much pizza is left?

_____

Multiply a 3-Digit Number by a 1-Digit Number

CA Standards
KEY NS 2.4, MR 2.1

Solve.

1. The school store sold 4 boxes of pencils last week. Each box had 112 pencils. How many pencils did the store sell last week?

_____

2. Enough pencils are produced on Earth each year to circle the moon about 225 times! How many times could the pencils produced in 3 years circle the moon?

_____

3. In a package of pencils, 8 are yellow and 4 are blue. How many yellow pencils are in 426 packages?

_____

4. An art supply store sold 243 boxes of pencils last year. Each box cost $3. How much money did the store receive for the pencils sold last year?

_____

5. A single pencil can draw a line equal to the length of 616 football fields! If you wanted to draw a line equal to the length of about 3,000 football fields, would you need 3, 4, or 5 pencils? Explain.

_____

_____

6. The school store has 3,000 pencils. They want to stock an eraser for each pencil. The erasers come in bags of 250. The store ordered 9 bags. Will they have an eraser for each pencil? Explain.

_____

_____

Regroup More than Once

CA Standard
KEY NS 2.4

Find the product. Regroup if needed.

Find 6 × 163.

Step 1 Multiply ones.

$6 \times 3 = 18$

Regroup 18 ones as 1 ten 8 ones.

$$\begin{array}{r} 1 \\ 163 \\ \times \ 6 \\ \hline 8 \end{array}$$

Step 2 Multiply tens.

$6 \times 6 = 36$

Add the 1 regrouped ten.

$36 + 1 = 37$

Regroup 37 tens as 3 hundreds 7 tens.

$$\begin{array}{r} 31 \\ 163 \\ \times \ 6 \\ \hline 78 \end{array}$$

Step 3 Multiply hundreds.

$6 \times 1 = 6$

Add the 3 regrouped hundreds. $6 + 3 = 9$

Solution:

$$\begin{array}{r} 31 \\ 163 \\ \times \ 6 \\ \hline 978 \end{array}$$

1. $\begin{array}{r} 134 \\ \times \ 4 \\ \hline \end{array}$

2. $\begin{array}{r} 214 \\ \times \ 6 \\ \hline \end{array}$

3. $\begin{array}{r} 431 \\ \times \ 5 \\ \hline \end{array}$

4. $\begin{array}{r} 248 \\ \times \ 2 \\ \hline \end{array}$

5. $\begin{array}{r} 531 \\ \times \ 3 \\ \hline \end{array}$

6. $\begin{array}{r} 2,116 \\ \times \ 3 \\ \hline \end{array}$

7. $\begin{array}{r} 1,187 \\ \times \ 3 \\ \hline \end{array}$

8. $\begin{array}{r} 2,083 \\ \times \ 4 \\ \hline \end{array}$

9. $\begin{array}{r} 5,210 \\ \times \ 9 \\ \hline \end{array}$

10. $\begin{array}{r} 9,711 \\ \times \ 7 \\ \hline \end{array}$

11. $8 \times 534 =$ _____

12. $4 \times 123 =$ _____

13. $5 \times 4,152 =$ _____

14. $2 \times 3,081 =$ _____

Spiral Review (Chapter 18, Lesson 4) **KEY AF 2.1**

Find the function rule and complete the function table.

	Input	Output
15.	$3.00	
	$4.19	$5.69
16.	$5.20	

17. What is the rule for the table?

_____

Regroup More than Once

CA Standard
KEY NS 2.4

The first public library in the United States opened in New England in 1948. The table below shows the number of public libraries in New England today.

Use the table to find the product. Regroup if necessary.

1. If every public library in Rhode Island has 8 atlases, how many atlases do the libraries have in all?

_____

2. In each public library in Vermont has 2 sets of encyclopedias, how many sets do they have in all?

_____

New England Public Libraries	
State	**Number of Libraries**
Maine	276
Massachusetts	480
New Hampshire	238
Rhode Island	72
Connecticut	242
Vermont	195

3. If each public library in New Hampshire and Rhode Island has 4 computers, what is the total number of computers in those libraries?

_____

4. If 6 librarians work in each public library in Connecticut and 8 librarians work in each public library in Maine, which state has more librarians?

_____

5. Massachusetts ordered 5 new desks for each of its public libraries. Joan says that 2,000 desks were ordered in all. What is wrong with Joan's calculation?

_____

_____

6. Connecticut ordered 7 new software programs for each public library. Maine ordered 5 new software programs for each public library. Each software program cost $29. Write a mathematical sentence that tells which state spent more money.

_____

_____

Multiply Money

Find the product.

$3.29
×   3

$\overset{2}{\$3.29}$
×   3
—————
$9.87

$3.29 × 3 = $9.87

Find the product. Regroup if necessary.

1. $1.73
   ×   2

2. $2.88
   ×   3

3. $3.66
   ×   2

4. $1.29
   ×   4

5. $4.29
   ×   4

6. $3.15
   ×   5

7. $2.68
   ×   8

8. $4.01
   ×   6

9. $9 × \$1.11 =$

10. $5 × \$3.16 =$

11. $4 × \$2.03 =$

12. $6 × \$1.32 =$

13. $5 × \$4.61 =$

14. $7 × \$1.68 =$

Spiral Review   (Chapter 20, Lesson 1) **KEY NS 2.4**

Solve.

15. $34 × 2 =$ _____

16. $13 × 3 =$ _____

17. Mr. Samuels wants to order 2 ant farms for every classroom. There are 14 classrooms. How many ant farms should he order?

_____

Name _____ Date _____

Multiply Money

Use the table to find the product. Regroup if necessary.

1. Which item was invented most recently? How much will 7 boxes of that item cost in all?

_____

Overall Stuff Store		
Item	Year Invented	Price for 1 box
Battery	1800	$4.19
Light Bulb	1878	$3.79
Paper Clip	1889	$1.75
Pushpin	1900	$3.15
Safety Pin	1849	$2.99
Tape	1923	$1.27
Zipper	1913	$9.25

2. Donne bought 4 boxes of batteries for her camping trip. How much did she spend in all?

_____

3. Cameron bought 3 boxes of safety pins. He paid with a ten-dollar bill. How much change did he receive?

_____

4. Shante is buying 8 light bulbs for the track lighting in her kitchen. If each box has 4 light bulbs, how much will she spend in all?

_____

5. Fran did the multiplication at the right to find how much 4 boxes of pushpins will cost. What mistake did she make?

$3.15
× 4
$1.260

_____

6. Terrance found the costs of 4 boxes of paper clips, 3 boxes of tape, and 1 box of zippers. He wrote this mathematical sentence: $9.25 > $6.80 > $3.81. What did Terrance do wrong?

_____

Name _____ Date _____

Make a Table

CA Standards
MR 2.3, KEY AF 2.1

**Make a table to solve each problem. Explain why your
answer makes sense.**

Mr. Murphy is setting up chairs for an assembly in the gym. He has placed 12
chairs in each row. There are 8 rows in all. How many chairs is Mr. Murphy setting
up altogether?

Step 1 Decide if you can make a table to
solve the problem. Making a table can help
you solve this problem. Next, decide what will
be in the first column and what will be in the
second column of the table. Here, column 1
might be labeled Number of Rows (Input).
Column 2 might be labeled Number of Chairs
(Output).

Step 2 Make the table. You can multiply
the number of rows by 12 or add 12 for each
additional row.

Solution: The 8 rows will contain 96 chairs.

Number of Rows (Input)	Number of Chairs (Output)
1	12
2	24
3	36
4	48
5	60
6	72
7	84
8	96

1. Yolanda plays basketball in a youth league. Each game is made
   up of 4 quarters, and each quarter is 8 minutes long. If Yolanda
   plays every quarter during 7 games, how many minutes does she
   play in all?

   _____

2. There are 6 teams in the youth basketball league. During the
   season, each team plays 15 games. How many total quarters
   of basketball are played in all of the teams' games during the season?

   _____

Spiral Review (Chapter 19, Lessons 1–2) **KEY NS 2.4**

Find the product.

3. 3 × 90 _____   **4.** 5 × 700 _____

Make a Table

Make a table to solve each problem.

1. Rizwan counted 15 pickets on a section of fence. How many pickets are there on 7 sections of fence?

   _____

2. The bells on a clock in Amber's house ring 4 times each hour. How many times do they ring during 12 hours?

   _____

3. The wipers on a car's windshield move every 12 seconds. How many times would they move during the course of 2 minutes?

   _____

4. On a mural, Miranda painted 16 trees. Each tree showed 9 leaves. How many leaves did she paint in all?

   _____

5. Jaime knows that there are 130 paper clips in a box. A package contains 8 boxes of paper clips. How many paper clips are there in a package?

   _____

6. Raychelle is comparing different types of photo albums. One album holds 6 photos on each page. The album comes with 112 pages. How many photos will fit in the album?

   _____

Hands On: Organize Data

CA Standards
KEY SDAP 1.3, SDAP 1.4

How many students have brown eyes?

Count the tally marks.
Remember that ||||| stands for 5.

$$5 + 5 + 2 = 12$$

Solution: Twelve students have brown eyes.

Students' Eye Color		
Color	Tally	Number
Blue	||||	5
Brown	|||| |||| ||	12
Green	||||	5

Use the tally chart in the box above for Problems 1 and 2.

1. How many students have either blue eyes or green eyes?

_____

2. How many more students have brown eyes than green eyes?

_____

Ask family members what color eyes they have. Write the results on the tally chart. Then use your tally chart for Problems 3 and 4.

3. How many people were surveyed?

_____

4. How many members of your family have brown eyes?

_____

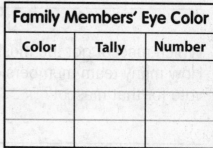

Family Members' Eye Color		
Color	Tally	Number

Spiral Review (Chapter 3, Lesson 2) **KEY AF 1.1**, (Chapter 18, Lesson 2) **KEY NS 3.3**

Write >, <, or = for each ◯.

5. $33 + 26$ ◯ $41 + 16$

6. $81 - 39$ ◯ $90 - 48$

7. Mike bought a banana for $0.79 and an apple for $1.25. How much did Mike spend in all?

_____

Hands On: Organize Data

CA Standards
KEY SDAP 1.3, SDAP 1.4

Complete the tally chart below to record the information
in the list. Then use the chart to solve each problem.

Votes for Team Mascot		
Mascot	**Tally**	**Number**
Bulldog		
Dolphin		
Lion		
Tiger		

Our Choices for Our Team Mascot	
Kim	Dolphin
Phillip	Bulldog
Anita	Lion
Roy	Tiger
Allen	Dolphin
Melissa	Lion
Toby	Lion
Sheera	Tiger
Carlos	Bulldog
Mark	Lion
Caroline	Dolphin
Brent	Lion

1. How many team members were surveyed in all?

   _____

2. How many team members voted for a bulldog or a dolphin?

   _____

3. Which mascot got the most votes? How many team members did **NOT** vote for that mascot?

   _____

4. How many people voted for a mascot with four legs?

   _____

5. Roy says that the tiger got the fewest votes for the team's mascot. Why is he wrong?

   _____

   _____

6. Anita transferred to another school. Then four new people joined the team. These were their votes: Salim, tiger; Cleon, dolphin; Gwen, bulldog; Emmy, tiger. Now which mascot is the favorite?

   _____

   _____

Line Plots

CA Standards
KEY SDAP 1.3, SDAP 1.4

How many players stole 2 or more bases?

The numbers at the bottom of the line plot stand for the number of bases stolen. Each X stands for 1 player.

Since the question asks how many players stole 2 or more bases, count the number of Xs above 2, 3, 4, and 5.

$3 + 2 + 1 = 6$ players

Solution: Six players stole 2 or more bases.

Bases Stolen Last Season

```
X              X
X              X
X    X    X    X
X    X    X    X         X
0    1    2    3    4    5
```

Use the data in the table to make a line plot on a separate sheet of paper. Use the line plot to answer Problems 1–3.

1. How many players scored exactly 2 touchdowns?

   _____

2. How many players scored more than 3 touchdowns?

   _____

3. How many players scored fewer than 3 touchdowns?

   _____

Touchdowns Scored Last Season			
John	3	Bill	2
Samantha	0	Jason	4
Charles	3	Denzell	3
Jack	4	Rachel	2
Timothy	1	Jessica	0
Michelle	6	David	3
Patricia	5	Juan	5

Spiral Review (Chapter 5, Lessons 3–4) **KEY** NS 2.2

Find the product.

4. $2 \times 5 =$ _____

5. $5 \times 9 =$ _____

6. Paul has 4 jars with 8 seashells in each jar. How many seashells does Paul have in all?

   _____

Line Plots

CA Standards
KEY SDAP 1.3, SDAP 1.4

The line plot below shows the number of touchdowns that
were scored in each Super Bowl game from 1990 to 2002.
Use the line plot to answer.

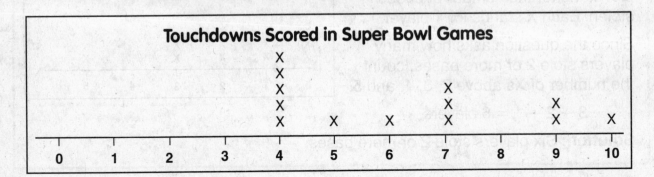

1. In how many of the Super Bowls
were exactly 5 touchdowns scored?

_____

2. In how many of the games were
more than 7 touchdowns scored?

_____

3. The 1995 Super Bowl had the
greatest number of touchdowns.
How many touchdowns were scored
during that game?

_____

4. What is the difference between
the greatest and fewest number of
touchdowns scored?

_____

5. In how many of the games were
fewer than 6 touchdowns scored?

_____

6. In how many Super Bowls were
an even number of touchdowns
scored?

_____

Hands On: Pictographs

CA Standards
KEY SDAP 1.3, MR 2.0

How many votes were there for handstands?

Each 👤 stands for 2 votes.

There are $2\frac{1}{2}$ 👤.

$2 + 2 + 1 = 5$

There were 5 votes for handstands.

Favorite Floor Exercises	
Splits	👤 👤 👤 👤 👤
Flips	👤 👤 👤
Cartwheels	👤 👤
Handstands	👤 👤 ⌐

Each 👤 stands for 2 votes.

Use the table to complete a pictograph on a separate sheet of paper. Use this key: Each ◆ stands for 4 players.
Use the pictograph to answer the questions.

1. How many ◆ did you draw for first grade?

   _____

2. Which grade had 6 ◆?

   _____

3. If 12 more fourth-grade students played, how many ◆ would there be for fourth grade in all?

   _____

Field Day Players	
Grade	**Number**
First	12
Second	20
Third	24
Fourth	8
Fifth	16

Spiral Review (Chapter 17, Lessons 2 and 3) **NS 3.0, NS 3.4**

Write a fraction and a decimal for the shaded part.

4. _____

5. _____

6. Willa finished $\frac{3}{10}$ of her math problems. Ginny finished 0.35 of her problems. Who finished more?

   _____

Hands On: Pictographs

The table shows the number of gold medals that each of the top four countries won at the 2000 Summer Olympic Games held in Sydney, Australia.

Olympic Gold Medals Won	
Country	Number of Medals
Australia	16
China	28
Russia	32
United States	40

1. Make a pictograph of the data in the table. Choose a symbol that stands for 4 gold medals.

2. How many symbols did you draw for China in your pictograph? Why?

3. For which country did you draw the most symbols? Why?

4. Why is 4 a good choice for the number of gold medals that each symbol stands for in the pictograph?

5. Germany won 13 gold medals in the 2000 Summer Olympics. How would you display this data on the pictograph?

6. The Netherlands won 20 fewer gold medals than Russia. How would you show the Netherlands' data on the pictograph?

Hands On: Bar Graphs

CA Standards
KEY SDAP 1.3, MR 2.3

How many more medals did Greece win than Denmark?

Find the values of the bar for Greece and the bar for Denmark.

The bar for Greece reaches to 8. The bar for Denmark reaches to 6.
$8 - 6 = 2$

Solution: Greece won 2 more medals than Denmark.

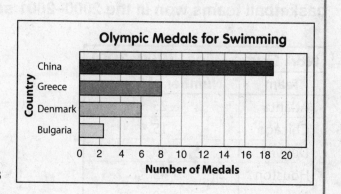

Use the data in the table to make a vertical bar graph on a separate piece of paper.
Use the bar graph to solve the problems.

Bats Joey Saw	
Type of Bat	**Number**
Fruit bat	15
Vampire bat	6
Long-nosed bat	13
Brown bat	9

1. What is the graph about?

_____

2. What is the scale on your graph?

_____

3. Of which type of bat did Joey see the fewest?

_____

Spiral Review (Chapter 19, Lesson 3) **MR 2.5**

Estimate the product. Round the larger factor to its greatest place.

4. $324 \times 3 =$ _____

5. $4 \times 76 =$ _____

6. Rodney practiced the tuba for 46 minutes each day on Monday, Wednesday, and Friday. Estimate how many minutes Rodney practiced in all.

_____

Name _____ Date _____

Hands On: Bar Graphs

CA Standards
KEY SDAP 1.3, MR 2.3

The table below shows the number of games some NBA basketball teams won in the 2000–2001 season.

NBA Game Wins, 2000–2001	
Team	**Number of Games**
Atlanta	25
Chicago	15
Denver	40
Houston	45
Miami	50

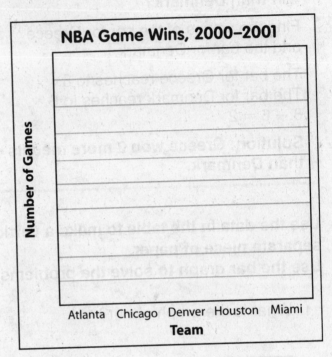

NBA Game Wins, 2000–2001

Number of Games

Atlanta Chicago Denver Houston Miami
Team

1. Use the grid to the right to make a bar graph of the data in this table. Use a scale of 5.

2. What is the greatest number on your scale? What is the least number?

_____

3. Which bar on your graph is the shortest? Why?

_____

_____

4. List the teams in order from most wins to fewest wins.

_____

_____

5. Which team won half as many games as Miami won? How can you tell from your graph?

_____

_____

6. Would your data change if you used a scale of 10 in the graph? Explain.

_____

_____

_____

Use with text pp. 482–483

Choose a Graph to Display Data

CA Standards
KEY SDAP 1.3, MR 1.0

This graph shows the number of students who were absent from school in 1 month.

How many students were absent in week 1?

Count the ☹ s in the pictograph:
2 ☹ s = 4 students.

Solution: 4 students were absent.

Students Absent	
Week	**Number**
1	☹ ☹
2	☹
3	☹ ☹
4	☹ ☹ ☹

Each ☹ Stands for 2 students

Use the graph above to solve the problems.

1. In which week were the most students absent?

_____

2. In which week were the fewest students absent?

_____

3. How many students were absent in all?

_____

4. How many students would $2\frac{1}{2}$ ☹ stand for?

_____

Spiral Review (Chapter 21, Lessons 2, 3) **KEY** NS 2.4

Find each product.

5. 141 × 6 = _____

6. 256 × 2 = _____

7. A gross is 144 items. Steve's Sporting Goods has 3 gross of softballs. How many softballs does the store have in all?

_____

Name _____ Date _____

Choose a Graph to Display Data

Write *line plot, tally chart, pictograph, or bar graph* to tell the best kind of graph to use. (You can choose more than one kind of graph as an answer.)

1. You want to show the results of a survey about people's favorite ice cream flavor.

   _____

   _____

2. You want to compare the lengths of the world's 10 longest rivers.

   _____

   _____

3. You want to show how many times members of the softball team from another school struck out.

   _____

   _____

4. You want to compare the kinds of pets your classmates have. You love to draw!

   _____

   _____

5. You want to show the results of a survey about your friends' hobbies. Which kind of graph is **not** a good choice?

   _____

   _____

6. The numbers you want to show on a graph are 5, 11, 33, 40, and 57. Which is the better graph to use, bar graph or pictograph?

   _____

   _____

Name _____ Date _____

Use a Graph

CA Standard
MR 2.0

Use the pictograph to solve each problem.

A teacher asked students to choose one of five activities as their favorite. Then she made a pictograph to show the results. How many students did the teacher survey?

Favorite Winter Activities	
Sledding	❄❄❄❄❄
Skiing	❄❄
Snow Sculptures	❄❄❄❄
Snowshoeing	❄❄

Each ❄ stands for 2 children

Step 1 Figure out what information you need from the graph. You need to find the total number of students who were surveyed about their favorite winter activity.

Step 2 Check to see what each snowflake stands for. In this graph, a snowflake stands for 2 students, and a half snowflake stands for 1 student. Count the number of snowflakes for each activity. Next to "Sledding," there are $4\frac{1}{2}$ snowflakes, so 9 students chose that activity.

Step 3 Repeat for each activity. Then add the numbers to find the total.

Solution: The teacher asked 23 students in all.

1. Write an equation to show the difference between the most popular winter activity and the least popular winter activity. _____

2. A class is planning a Winter Activities Day. Which is a better choice for a schedule of winter activities? Why?

   A skiing, snowshoeing, and sledding

   B sledding, snow sculptures, and snowshoeing

   _____

   _____

Spiral Review (Chapter 18, Lesson 2) **KEY NS 3.3**

3. $2.76
   + $4.47

4. $38.03
   + $29.59

5. Hank has $14.85 in a bank account before making a deposit of $6.20. How much money does he have in the bank account now?

   _____

Name _____ Date _____

Use a Graph

Use the line plot or bar graph to solve each problem.
Explain why your answer makes sense.

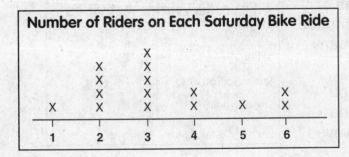

1. What was the most common number of riders on a Saturday ride?

_____

2. How many Saturday rides does the graph illustrate?

_____

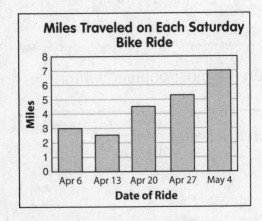

3. Which was the date of the shortest ride?

_____

4. Which two rides were the most similar in length?

_____

Most Common Ways to Get to School	
Walking	🏠🏠🏠🏠🏠🏠🏠🏠🏠🏠🏠
Riding a bike	🏠🏠🏠🏠🏠🏠
Riding in a car	🏠🏠🏠🏠🏠
Riding in a bus	🏠🏠🏠🏠🏠🏠🏠🏠🏠
Each 🏠 stands for 4 students	

5. What is the difference between the number of students who walk and the number of students who ride in a car to school?

_____

6. How many students are counted in this graph?

_____

Hands On: Record Outcomes

CA Standards
KEY SDAP 1.2, KEY SDAP 1.3

Use the spinner to answer each question.

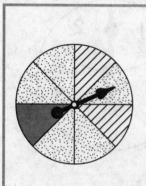

Example

How many possible outcomes are there?

Each space has dots, stripes, or shading.

Solution

There are 3 possible outcomes.

1. Which space are you most likely to land on?

_____

2. Which space are you least likely to land on?

_____

Trey spun a spinner 20 times. He landed on brown 12 times, blue 5 times, and green 3 times. Use the information given and fill in the table below.

Color	Tally	Number
Brown		
Blue		
Green		

Use the tally chart to answer questions 3–4.

3. If Trey spins the spinner again, what color is he most likely to land on?

_____

4. If Trey spins the spinner again, what color is he least likely to land on?

_____

Spiral Review (Chapter 21, Lesson 3) **KEY NS 2.4**

Solve.

5. 5 × 122 _____

6. 8 × 427 _____

7. Sal is counting change. If he has 5 bags of pennies with 125 pennies in each bag, how many pennies does he have in total?

_____

Name _____ Date _____

Hands On: Record Outcomes

CA Standards
KEY SDAP 1.2, KEY SDAP 1.3

Use the spinner at the right to answer problems 1–4.

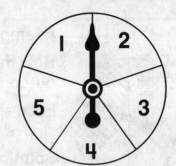

1. How many possible outcomes are there for each spin? What are those outcomes?

   _____

   _____

2. You spin the spinner twice. The sum of both spins' numbers is one outcome. How could you find all the possible outcomes?

   _____

   _____

3. If you spin the spinner twice, how many ways are there to get a sum of spins equal to 6? _____

4. If you spin the spinner and roll a six-sided die, is it possible to get a total of 12?

   _____

   _____

Kendra has two of the spinners shown above. She spins both spinners 100 times. Each time, she records the sum of the two spins' numbers. The results of her experiment are recorded in the table. Use the table to answer Questions 5–6.

Spinning Two Spinners									
Outcome	2	3	4	5	6	7	8	9	10
Number of Occurrences	4	7	10	15	23	17	11	8	5

5. How many possible outcomes are there? Why is 1 NOT a possible outcome for the experiment?

   _____

   _____

   _____

6. Which outcome occurred most often in Kendra's experiment? Why do you think this outcome occurred most often?

   _____

   _____

   _____

   _____

Name _____ Date _____

Probability

CA Standard
KEY SDAP 1.1

**Write the word *certain, likely, unlikely,* or *impossible*
to describe the probability of picking a black circle.**

Example

If you picked a circle,
it would probably be
black.

Solution

The probability of
picking a black
circle is *likely*.

1.  _____

2.  _____

3.  _____

**Write whether the event is *certain, likely, unlikely,* or
impossible. Explain your answer.**

4. You will win a trip to Paris, France. _____

5. A dog can fly. _____

6. The day after Sunday is Monday. _____

7. You will be awake at 12:00 noon. _____

Draw a set of shapes to represent the statement.

8. Picking a square is unlikely.

Spiral Review (Chapter 20, Lessons 3–4) **KEY** NS 2.4

Find the product.

9. $6 \times 22 =$ _____

10. $7 \times 19 =$ _____

11. Bart has 8 packages of candy with 16 pieces of candy in each package. How
many pieces of candy does Bart have?

_____

Name _____ Date _____

Probability

CA Standard
SDAP 1.1

Use the spinner at the right to answer problems 1–6.

1. On which color is the spinner likely to land? Why?

_____

_____

2. On which color is the spinner least likely to land? Why?

_____

_____

3. You spin the spinner once. Describe a certain event. Explain why you can describe your event that way.

_____

_____

_____

_____

_____

_____

4. Why is it possible, but unlikely, that the spinner will land on green?

_____

_____

_____

_____

_____

5. If you know that an event is likely or unlikely, what other word can you use to describe the event? Explain how you know.

_____

_____

_____

6. How could you change the spinner to make it impossible to land on yellow?

_____

_____

_____

Hands On: Make Predictions

Example

Jen is pulling marbles out of a bag. The results are recorded in the table below.

Color	Number of Times
Blue	11
Green	2
Red	4

What color is Jen most likely to draw next?

Think: She already drew 11 blue marbles. There are probably more blue marbles in the bag.

Solution:

She will probably draw a blue marble.

Use the table below to answer the following questions.

1. How many cashews were drawn? _____

2. Which nut is least likely to be drawn next? _____

3. Which nut is most likely to be drawn next? _____

Type of Nut	Number of Times Drawn
Almond	5
Brazil Nut	2
Cashew	6
Peanut	15
Pistachio	4

Spiral Review (Chapter 18, Lesson 4) **AF 2.0, KEY AF 2.1**

4. Find the function rule for the table below. _____

Input (Number of ice cream cones)	Price
1	$2
2	$4
3	$6

Hands On: Make Predictions

CA Standards
SDAP 1.4, KEY SDAP 1.3

Leah is randomly picking marbles from a bag that only contains blue, green, red, and white marbles. The results are recorded in the bar graph below.

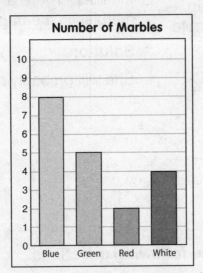

Number of Marbles

1. What is the total number of marbles Leah took from the bag?

_____

2. How many more blue marbles than red marbles were drawn from the bag?

_____

3. Which color is the least likely to be picked next?

_____

4. Which color is the most likely to be picked next?

_____

5. What is the likelihood of picking a yellow marble from the bag?

_____

6. If twelve red marbles and eight blue marbles are added to the bag, which marble is most likely to be picked next?

_____

_____

_____

Make Predictions

CA Standards
SDAP 1.4, KEY SDAP 1.3

The tally chart shows the results of picking objects from a bag 8 times and replacing them each time.

Example

What object do you predict will be picked next?

Solution

I predict a triangle will be picked text.

Picking Objects from a Box		
Outcome	Tally	Number
Triangle	$\cancel{IIII}\ I$	6
Square	II	2

Use the tally chart at the right for Questions 1–2.

1. What object do you predict will be pulled from the box next?

   _____

2. What object do you predict is least likely to be pulled from the box?

   _____

Objects Pulled from a Box		
Outcome	Tally	Number
Star	II	2
Sun	$\cancel{IIII}\ I$	6
Moon	I	1

Perry picked a colored square out of a bag and returned it 20 times. He recorded the results in a bar graph. Use the graph to answer Questions 3–4.

3. How many times did Perry pick each color?

   _____

4. What color do you predict he will pick next?

   _____

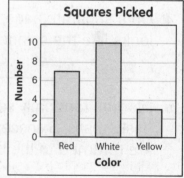

Spiral Review (Chapter 22, Lesson 4) **KEY** SDAP 1.3

Use the bar graph to answer the questions below.

5. How many runs did Jack score in the game? _____

6. How many more runs did Jack score than Ahmed? _____

7. What is the total number of runs for the entire team? _____

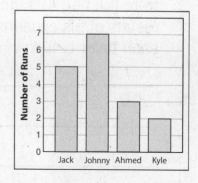

Name _____ Date _____

Make Predictions

CA Standards
SDAP 1.4, KEY SDAP 1.3

Rita spun a spinner 30 times and recorded the results on the bar graph at the right. Use the graph to answer problems 1–3.

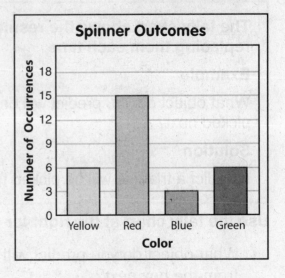

Spinner Outcomes

1. How many times did she spin yellow?

   _____

2. What is the least likely outcome for the next spin? Explain why.

   _____

   _____

3. What is a likely prediction for the color she will spin next? Explain your thinking.

   _____

   _____

4. On a separate page, draw and color an example of a spinner that probably looks like the spinner Rita used in her experiment.

   _____

5. Martine randomly selects 20 balls from a bag of 40 balls. She picks 8 basketballs, 5 soccer balls, 4 footballs, and 3 tennis balls. If the 5 soccer balls are returned to the bag, predict what type of ball will be picked next.

   _____

6. A bag has 10 tennis balls that are three different colors. Chaz picks a ball from the bag 40 times without looking and returns it to the bag each time. The results of his experiment are 4 pink, 21 yellow, and 15 purple. How many of each color ball do you think are in the bag? Explain your answers.

   _____

   _____

Name _____ Date _____

Hands On: Equal Groups

Divide the 13 counters into two equal groups. How many counters
are left over?

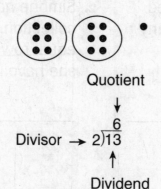

Quotient
↓
$\begin{array}{r} 6 \\ 2\overline{)13} \end{array}$
Divisor →   ↑
Dividend

Solution: There are two equal groups of six with 1 counter left over.

Use counters to complete the table.

	Division	Dividend	Divisor	Quotient	Number Left Over
1.	$3\overline{)19}$				
2.	$5\overline{)39}$				
3.	$8\overline{)42}$				
4.	$6\overline{)29}$				
5.	$4\overline{)27}$				
6.	$7\overline{)34}$				

Spiral Review (Chapter 3, Lesson 2; Chapter 5, Lesson 3; Chapter 6, Lesson 4; Chapter 20,
Lessons 1 and 2) **KEY AF 1.1**, **KEY NS 2.2**, **KEY NS 2.4**

7. Write >, <, or = for the ◯. Tell if the number sentence is an
equation or an inequality.

37 + 13 ◯ 31 + 15 _____

8. 7
     ×5
     ___

9. Elise has 3 bags of peanuts.
Each bag has 12 peanuts. How
many peanuts are there in all?

_____

Hands On: Equal Groups

CA Standard
NS 2.0

Use counters to solve the problems.

1. Hector has 39 stickers. He placed them into 6 equal piles. How many stickers did he have left over?

2. Simone has 44 buttons in her collection. She lined them up into 8 equal rows. How many buttons did she have left over?

3. Melissa has 38 dyed eggs. She wants to store them in cartons of 12 eggs each. How many cartons will be full? How many eggs will be in the carton that is not full?

4. Liam organized 28 video games in boxes. He put 5 games in each box. How many full boxes does he have? How many video games are in the box that is not full?

5. Tyrone used counters to model the division problem: $37 \div 5$. He came up with the quotient of 6 with 7 left over. What's wrong with Tyrone's answer?

6. Tara divided by 5 and got the quotient was 6 with 2 left over, and she was correct. What is the dividend of the problem?

Hands On: Repeated Subtraction

CA Standard
NS 2.0

Use repeated subtraction to solve division problems with some numbers left over.

Find 17 ÷ 4.

• How many full groups did you remove? 4

• How many counters are left over? 1

Solution: 17 ÷ 4 = 4 with 1 left over

Use counters and repeated subtraction to complete the table.

	Division	Number (dividend)	Number of Equal Groups (divisor)	Number in Each Group (quotient)	Number Left Over
1.	7)45				
2.	3)33				
3.	2)39				
4.	9)89				
5.	8)71				
6.	5)44				
7.	6)43				
8.	4)67				

Spiral Review (Chapter 19, Lesson 3) **MR 2.4**

Estimate each product. Round the greater factor to its greatest place.

9. 58 × 3 _____

10. 67 × 4 _____

11. A music store sells 589 CDs a day. About how many CDs does the music store sell in 5 days?

_____

Hands On: Repeated Subtraction

Use counters and repeated subtraction to solve the problems.

1. Alvin brought 19 peaches home. He divided them equally into 5 paper bags. How many peaches were left over?

   _____

2. Shelby brought 29 peaches home. She divided them into 3 boxes to give to her friends. How many peaches were left over?

   _____

3. Ezra has to plant 73 peach trees. He can plant 8 peach trees a day. How many days can Ezra plant 8 trees? How many trees will he plant on the day after his last 8-tree day?

   _____

4. At Ray's Peach Farm, 56 peaches are being packed in boxes. Each box has 9 peaches. How many full boxes are needed to hold the peaches? How many peaches will be in the box after his last 9-peach box?

   _____

5. Hakim has 53 peaches. He has a week and 1 day to sell his peaches. If he sells an equal number of peaches each day, how many peaches will Hakim sell a day? How many peaches will remain unsold?

   _____

6. Reza would like to sell 60 full boxes of peaches a week. Each box contains 8 peaches, 4 rows with 2 peaches each. If she sells 8 full boxes each day, how many full boxes will she sell in a week?

   _____

Total Cost and Unit Cost

CA Standards
MR 2.4, NS 2.7

Solve. Explain why your answer makes sense.

> Mr. Robbins bought 8 containers of orange juice for a class party. The total cost was $24. Each container was the same price. What was the unit cost?
>
> **Step 1** Write the information you know and the information you need to find.
>
> total cost = $24   number of items = 8   unit cost = $ _____
>
> total cost = number of items × unit cost
>
> **Step 2** Write a number sentence to find the unit price. To find the unit price, divide the total cost by the number of items.
> Mr. Robbins bought 8 items for a total cost of $24.
>
> $24 ÷ 8 = $3
>
> **Solution:** The unit cost was $3.

1. Nick bought 6 bags of dog food at the grocery store. All the bags were the same price. The total cost was $66. How much money did each bag of dog food cost? _____

2. One roll of film costs $4. Two rolls of film cost $8. Three rolls of film cost $12. If the cost increase remains the same, how much will 4 rolls of film cost? _____

3. The total cost for 5 kitchen stools is $75. Each kitchen stool is the same price. What is the unit cost? _____

Spiral Review (Chapter 3, Lesson 2) **KEY AF 1.1**

Write >, <, or = for each ◯. Tell if the number sentence is an equation or an inequality.

4. 24 + 28 ◯ 52 _____

5. 47 + 21 ◯ 42 + 27 _____

6. There are 12 boys and 13 girls in Mrs. Frank's classroom. There are 14 boys and 12 girls in Mrs. Jordan's classroom. Compare the number of students in the two classrooms. _____

Name _____ Date _____

Total Cost and Unit Cost

Solve. Explain why your answer makes sense.

1. The total cost of 5 boxes of rubber bands is $15. Each box of rubber bands is the same price. What is the unit cost?

_____

2. One package of pencils costs $3. Two packages of pencils cost $6. Three packages of pencils cost $9. If the cost increase remains the same, how much would 4 packages cost?

_____

3. The total cost of 4 staplers is $36. Each stapler is the same price. What is the unit cost?

_____

4. One package of 5 notebooks costs $8. Two packages cost $16. Three packages cost $24. If the cost increase of each package of 5 notebooks remains the same, how much would 4 packages cost?

_____

5. The total cost of 12 reams of paper is $30. Each ream of paper is the same price. What is the unit cost?

_____

6. One package of four ballpoint pens costs $5. A package of five ballpoint pens costs $6.25. A package of six ballpoint pens costs $7.50. If the cost increase remains the same, how much would a package of 8 ballpoint pens cost?

_____

Hands On: Divide 2-Digit Numbers

If 24 students are divided into 2 equal groups, how many students would be in each group?

Step Use base-ten blocks to show 24.

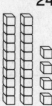

Step 2 Divide the tens into 2 equal groups.

Step 3 Divide the ones blocks into 2 equal groups.

Solution:

There are 2 equal groups of 12 blocks.

Use blocks to complete the table.

	Number	Number of Equal Groups	Number in Each Group	Show the Division
	30	3	10	$30 \div 3 = 10$
1.	44	4		
2.	22	2		
3.	66	3		

Spiral Review (Chapter 22, Lesson 1) **KEY** SDAP 1.3

Use the tally chart at the right for problems 4–5.

4. How many students were surveyed?

_____

5. Which instrument is the most popular? How do you know?

_____

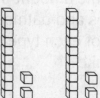

Favorite Musical Instrument

Instrument	Tally
Flute	ҢҢ l
Clarinet	ҢҢ lll
Trumpet	ҢҢ ll
Tuba	lll
Violin	llll

Hands On: Divide 2-Digit Numbers

Solve.

1. Mary baked 44 cookies. If she baked the same amount of chocolate chip cookies and oatmeal cookies, how many of each type of cookie did she bake?

2. Felix rode his bike 36 miles over the weekend. If he divided his trip into 3 equal parts, how many miles did he ride in each part?

3. Robert played the cello for 24 minutes after school. If he played 2 pieces that each lasted the same amount of time, how long was each piece?

4. Fabian took 25 cookies out of a box and placed an equal number of cookies on 4 plates. How many cookies were left over?

5. On each of three nights, Jordana read 23, 30 and 31 pages to finish reading half of her favorite book. If she must return the book to the library in 4 days, how many pages must she read per day to finish the book?

6. Melinda is arranging the desks in her classroom into groups she calls tables. She has 10 desks at the front of the classroom, 12 in the rear, and 14 desks in the middle of the room. She wants to create 3 tables with an equal number of desks in each table. How many desks will she put in each table?

Hands On: Regroup in Division

CA Standards
NS 2.5, MR 2.3

Find 42 ÷ 3.

Step 1 Use base-ten blocks to show 42.

Step 2 Divide the tens into 3 equal groups.

Step 3 Regroup the 1 leftover ten as 10 ones.

Step 4 Divide the 12 ones into 3 equal groups.

Solution:

There are 3 equal groups with 1 ten and 4 ones, or 10 + 4 = 14.

So 42 ÷ 3 = 14.

	Number	Number of Equal Groups	Number in Each Group	Show the Division
	36	3	12	36 ÷ 3 = 12
1.	84	4		
2.	60	5		
3.	75	3		
4.	56	2		

Spiral Review (Chapter 22, Lesson 3) **KEY** SDAP 1.3, MR 2.0

Use the table to the right to answer the following questions.

5. How many students were surveyed?

_____

6. If you were to construct a pictograph of the data, what would be an appropriate symbol to use to represent students? How many students would each symbol represent?

_____

Favorite Sports Among 3rd Graders	
Sport	**Number of Students**
Baseball	10
Football	18
Soccer	14
Volleyball	6
Tennis	8

Name _____ Date _____

Hands On: Regroup in Division

CA Standards
NS 2.5, MR 2.3

Solve.

1. Bettina used 40 yards of fabric to make 5 shirts. How many yards of fabric did she use on each shirt?

   _____

2. Teo bought 6 boxes of candy with 4 pieces in each box. If he evenly divided the candy to give to his 3 sisters, how many pieces did he give to each of his sisters?

   _____

3. Ms. Kang's kindergarten class has 10 boys and 10 girls. Ms. Kang wants to create 5 equal groups. How many students will be in each group?

   _____

4. Mara has 4 bags of 10 pennies and 8 additional pennies. How many pieces of 8-cent candy can she buy?

   _____

5. Ruby has 1 twenty-dollar bill, 2 ten-dollar bills and 6 singles. She wants to buy as many $3 bracelets as possible. What is the greatest number of $3 bracelets she can buy? How much money will she have left over?

   _____

   _____

6. Gabe is buying containers of ice cream that cost $5 each. He has 2 twenty-dollar bills, 1 ten and 7 singles. What is the greatest number of containers of ice cream he can buy? If he buys this number of containers, how many dollars will he have left?

   _____

   _____

Divide 2-Digit Numbers

CA Standards
NS 2.5, **KEY** NS 2.3

3)35

Step 1 Divide the tens into 3 equal groups.

11
3)35
−3
0

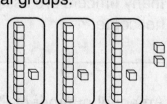

There are 3 groups of 1 ten.

Step 2 Divide the ones into 3 equal groups.

11
3)35
−3
05
− 3
2

There are 3 groups of 3 ones each with 2 ones left over.

Solution:

$35 \div 3 = 11$ R2

---

1. 5)59 **2.** 5)50 **3.** 4)82 **4.** 2)49 **5.** 4)46

6. $94 \div 3 =$ _____ **7.** $83 \div 2 =$ _____ **8.** $66 \div 6 =$ _____ **9.** $49 \div 4 =$ _____

Spiral Review (Chapter 24, Lessons 2–3) **NS 2.0, KEY NS 2.3**

Complete the table.

	Divison	What multiplication fact can you use?	Number of equal groups	Number left over
10.	4)27			
11.	7)69			

12. Wen has 35 photos. She wants to place 8 photos on each page of her album. How many complete pages of photos can she fill? How many photos will be leftover?

_____

Name _____ Date _____

Divide 2-Digit Numbers

Solve.

1. Each of the officers in the air support unit is assigned to one of 3 helicopters. How many officers are assigned to each helicopter?

_____

2. An equal number of D.A.R.E. officers are assigned to each of the 4 school districts in Capital City. How many D.A.R.E. officers serve each district?

_____

Capital City Police Special Units	
Unit	**Number of Officers**
Air Support	39
Bicycle Patrol	85
D.A.R.E.	84
K-9	36
Marine Patrol	20
Mounted Patrol	53
SWAT	68

3. The SWAT unit works in 6 teams. Officers not assigned to a team are on call that week. How many officers are on each SWAT team? How many are on call each week?

_____

4. The police department plans to double the size of the K-9 unit so that each precinct will have 8 K-9 officers. How many precincts are in the department?

_____

5. The mounted patrol unit will march in this year's police parade. The police chief wants them to march in equal rows of 5 officers. She figures that there will be 1 row with only 3 officers. Is the chief right? How do you know?

_____

_____

6. What if the mounted patrol and the marine patrol march together in the parade. How many rows of 5 officers will be in the parade? How many soldiers will be left over?

_____

Hands On: Divide 3-Digit Numbers

CA Standards
NS 2.5, MR 2.3

If Cherry Lane Elementary School has 189 students divided into 9 classes, how many students are in each class?

Step ① Use base-ten blocks to show 189.

Step ② Since there is only one hundreds block, convert it to 10 tens blocks.

Step ③ Divide the 18 tens blocks into 9 equal groups. There are 2 tens in each group.

Step ④ Divide the 9 ones into 9 equal groups. There is 1 ones block in each group.

Solution: There are 21 students in each class.

Complete the table.

	Number	Number of Equal Groups	Number in Each Group	Show the Division
	422	2	211	$2\overline{)422} = 211$
1.	633	3		
2.	515	5		
3.	404	4		
4.	927	9		

Spiral Review (Chapter 23, Lesson 1) **KEY** SDAP 1.2

Use the spinner at the right to answer 5 and 6.

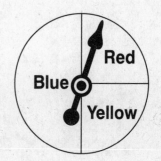

5. Which outcome do you think is the most likely?

_____

6. Which outcomes are equally likely?

_____

Name _____   Date _____

Hands On: Divide 3-Digit Numbers

CA Standards
NS 2.5, MR 2.3

Solve.

1. Anna has 232 jellybeans she wants to share with her brother. If she divides the jellybeans into 2 groups, how many jellybeans are in each group?

   _____

2. Brianna needs to divide a group of 484 tadpoles evenly into 4 fish tanks. How many tadpoles should go into each tank?

   _____

3. Gally ate a sandwich with 531 calories. If he ate the sandwich in 9 bites, how many calories did each bite of the sandwich contain?

   _____

4. Meli earned $248 by delivering the newspaper for 8 weeks. How much money did she earn each week?

   _____

5. Beth's parents are taking a 532 mile trip. On the first day they drove 28 miles. If they drive an equal number of miles on each of the remaining 4 days, how many miles must they drive on each of the following days?

   _____

6. Lindsay placed her collection of 654 coins into a display case. If each row of the display case has 8 coins, how many coins are not placed into a row? How many rows of coins are filled by coins?

   _____

Divide 3- and 4-Digit Numbers

CA Standards
NS 2.5, MR 2.2

Divide and check.

Example

$3\overline{)379}$

Step 1 Divide the hundreds.

$$\begin{array}{r} 1 \\ 3\overline{)379} \\ -3 \\ \hline 0 \end{array}$$

Step 2 Bring down the tens. Divide the tens.

$$\begin{array}{r} 12 \\ 3\overline{)379} \\ -3\downarrow \\ \hline 07 \\ -6 \\ \hline 1 \end{array}$$

Step 3 Regroup leftover tens as ones.

$$\begin{array}{r} 12 \\ 3\overline{)379} \\ -3 \\ \hline 07 \\ -6\downarrow \\ \hline 19 \end{array}$$

Step 4 Divide the ones.

$$\begin{array}{r} 126\ R1 \\ 3\overline{)379} \\ -3 \\ \hline 07 \\ -6 \\ \hline 19 \\ -18 \\ \hline 1 \end{array}$$

Solution: 379 ÷ 3 = 126 R1

1. $3\overline{)681}$ 2. $4\overline{)496}$ 3. $2\overline{)232}$ 4. $5\overline{)567}$ 5. $6\overline{)684}$

6. $6\overline{)643}$ 7. $4\overline{)848}$ 8. $3\overline{)639}$ 9. $3\overline{)377}$ 10. $4\overline{)884}$

11. $595 \div 5$ 12. $856 \div 4$ 13. $672 \div 2$ 14. $834 \div 2$

_____   _____   _____   _____

Spiral Review (Chapter 21, Lessons 2 and 3) **KEY NS 2.4, MR 2.1**

Multiply.

15. 412×8 _____   16. 593×7 _____

17. Robyn ate a hamburger with 432 calories. How many calories are in 3 hamburgers?

_____

Divide 3- and 4-Digit Numbers

CA Standards
NS 2.5, MR 2.2

Solve

1. This month 342 volunteers will clean up 3 wetland areas. An equal number of volunteers will work in each area. How many volunteers will help clean up each wetland area?

_____

2. The Meals-on-Wheels volunteers deliver 791 meals each week. If they deliver meals each day of the week, how many meals do they deliver each day?

_____

3. There were 972 huggers volunteering at this year's Special Olympics. The same number of huggers worked at each of the 9 events, and each hugger worked at only one event. How many huggers volunteered at each event?

_____

4. **What's Wrong?** The third-graders collected 420 blankets this winter to give to homeless shelters. They gave the same number of blankets to 4 different shelters. Janet says that they gave 150 blankets to each shelter. What mistake did she make?

_____

_____

_____

5. Marianne divided her collection of 718 stuffed animals into groups of 4. She had 6 stuffed animals left over. How do you know that she made a mistake putting the stuffed animals into groups? Explain.

_____

_____

6. Kenny has 124 baseball cards. Mark has 432 baseball cards. They combined their collection to put into an album. Each row of the album contains 8 cards. How many rows are filled? How many cards are left over?

_____

_____

Divide Money

CA Standards
KEY NS 3.3, NS 2.7

Divide. Model with coins and bills if you wish.

3)$6.48

Step 1 Divide the dollars. Place the dollar sign in the quotient.

$$\begin{array}{r} \$2 \\ 3)\overline{\$6.48} \\ -6 \\ \hline 0 \end{array}$$

Step 2 Divide the dimes. Use a decimal point to separate the dollars and cents.

$$\begin{array}{r} \$2.1 \\ 3)\overline{\$6.48} \\ -6 \\ \hline 04 \\ -3 \\ \hline 1 \end{array}$$

Step 3 Divide the pennies.

$$\begin{array}{r} \$2.16 \\ 3)\overline{\$6.48} \\ -6 \\ \hline 04 \\ -3 \\ \hline 18 \\ -18 \\ \hline 0 \end{array}$$

Solution: $6.48 ÷ 3 = $2.16

1. 2)$8.54   2. 2)$4.78   3. 5)$9.95   4. 3)$9.57

Spiral Review (Chapter 23, Lesson 4) SDAP 1.4, **KEY** SDAP 1.3

The bar graph shows the results of Melania spinning a spinner 25 times. Use the graph to answer the following questions.

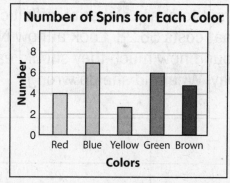

Number of Spins for Each Color

Number

Red Blue Yellow Green Brown

Colors

5. How many times did she spin each color?

_____

_____

6. Do you think the chance of spinning each color is equally likely?

_____

_____

7. If Melania keeps spinning the spinner, which colors do you think will be spun the least?

_____

Divide Money

CA Standards
KEY NS 3.3, NS 2.7

Solve each problem.

1. Bryant raised $9.45 on his first 3 calls for a charity telethon. Each caller pledged the same amount of money. How much did each caller donate to the charity?

_____

2. A pack of 4 cards at the charity bingo game cost $4.60. How much does each bingo card cost?

_____

3. The third-graders sold homemade dog biscuits to raise money for an animal shelter. They charged $2.58 for a box of 6 biscuits. How much did each biscuit cost?

_____

4. Alice sets aside the same amount of money each day to donate to charity. If she donates $8.40 each week to charity, how much money does she set aside each day?

_____

5. **What's Wrong?** Nina and 3 friends want to share a charity raffle ticket that costs $6.28. Look at how Nina found how much they should each pay. What did she do wrong?

_____

_____

_____

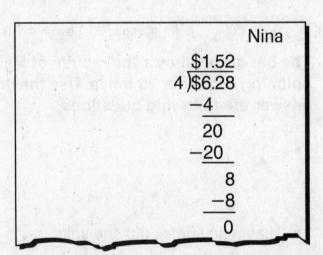

6. Beth bought three bags of apples for $3.38, $3.90, and $2.88. If she used the apples she purchased to make 8 apple pies, how much did she spend on apples for each apple pie?

_____

Place the First Digit

CA Standards
NS 2.5, (KEY) NS 2.3

Divide. Check your answers.

$6)\overline{246}$

Step 1 Divide the hundreds.

$2 < 6$

There are not enough hundreds to divide.

Go to the tens place.

Step 2 Divide the tens.

$$\begin{array}{r} 4 \\ 6)\overline{246} \\ -24 \\ \hline 0 \end{array}$$

Step 3 Bring down the ones. Divide the ones.

$$\begin{array}{r} 41 \\ 6)\overline{246} \\ -24\downarrow \\ \hline 06 \\ -\ 6 \\ \hline 0 \end{array}$$

Step 4 Check.

$$\begin{array}{r} 41 \\ \times\ 6 \\ \hline 246 \end{array}$$

Solution: $246 \div 6 = 41$

1. $5)\overline{445}$ 2. $6)\overline{312}$ 3. $9)\overline{558}$ 4. $3)\overline{177}$ 5. $2)\overline{196}$

Solve for *n*.

6. $488 \div 2 = n$ 7. $56 \div 2 = n$ 8. $272 \div 2 = n$ 9. $256 \div 2 = n$

   $488 \div 4 = n$ $56 \div 4 = n$ $272 \div 4 = n$ $256 \div 4 = n$

   $488 \div 8 = n$ $56 \div 8 = n$ $272 \div 8 = n$ $256 \div 8 = n$

_____   _____   _____   _____

Spiral Review   (Chapter 25, Lessons 2–3) **NS 2.5, MR 2.3**

Divide.

10. $5)\overline{42}$ 11. $8)\overline{77}$

_____   _____

12. Clayton placed 38 cupcakes into boxes. If 12 cupcakes fit into each box, how many cupcakes were leftover?

_____

Name _____ Date _____

Place the First Digit

CA Standards
NS 2.5, **KEY** NS 2.3

Use the table to solve each problem.

1. If all the firefighters in Wyoming are evenly divided into 3 large departments, how many firefighters are in each department?

_____

2. The North Dakota firefighters each volunteer one day a week for community service. If an equal number of firefighters volunteers each day, how many volunteer on Friday?

_____

3. The Idaho firefighters give fire safety demonstrations in 9 school districts. About how many firefighters give the demonstrations in each district?

_____

4. The state of Vermont is divided into 5 regions. If each region has an equal number of firefighters, how many work in each region?

_____

States with the Fewest Full-Time Firefighters	
State	**Number of Firefighters**
Alaska	586
Delaware	177
Idaho	934
Montana	524
North Dakota	301
South Dakota	389
Vermont	260
West Virginia	896
Wyoming	321

Show your work.

5. **Multistep** Each state divides its firefighters into groups of 4. One group from each state is sent to help fight a forest fire. How many firefighters from Montana and West Virginia will be sent in all? How did you find your answer?

_____

_____

6. **Multistep** The firefighters of North and South Dakota join the firefighters of Idaho and Montana to fight a fire in Saskatchewan. If the size of the fire is 4 acres, how many firefighters must be assigned to each acre?

_____

Name _____ Date _____

Problem Solving: Multistep Problems

CA Standards
NS 2.8, MR 1.2

Solve.

Angie bought a package of colored paper. The package had 8 sheets each of red, blue, and green paper. Angie used $\frac{1}{4}$ of the paper she bought. How many sheets of paper did Angie use?

Step 1 Find the total number of sheets.

$$\begin{array}{r} 8 \leftarrow \text{number of each color} \\ \times\ 3 \leftarrow \text{number of colors} \\ \hline 24 \leftarrow \text{total number of sheets} \end{array}$$

There are 24 sheets in all.

Step 2 Draw a picture to find $\frac{1}{4}$ of 24.

$\frac{1}{4}$ of 24 is 6.

Solution: Angie used 6 sheets of paper.

---

1. At the craft fair, Angie arranged origami figures in 5 rows with 6 figures in each row. She sold $\frac{2}{3}$ of the figures at the fair. How many figures did Angie sell at the craft fair?

2. Thomas bought a package of pencils. There were 5 pencils each of red, yellow, blue, and green. He took $\frac{1}{5}$ of the pencils to school. How many pencils did he take to school?

Spiral Review   (Chapter 23, Lesson 1) **KEY** SDAP 1.2

Use the spinner at the right to answer 3 and 4.

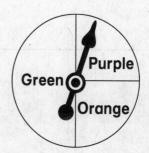

3. Which outcome do you think is the most likely?

4. Are any outcomes equally likely?

Problem Solving: Multistep Problems

CA Standards
NS 2.8, MR 1.2

Problem: Sharon bought 8 yards each of calico, polka dot, and denim material. She used $\frac{3}{4}$ of all the cloth to make pillows. How many yards of cloth did she use in all?

1. What information from the problem do you know?

_____

_____

_____

_____

2. What should your first step be to solve the problem?

_____

_____

_____

3. How many yards of cloth did Sharon buy in all?

_____

_____

4. What is $\frac{1}{4}$ of the total yards of cloth Sharon bought?

_____

_____

5. How many yards of cloth did Sharon use in all?

_____

6. How can using counters help you check that your answer is reasonable?

_____

_____

Hands On: Estimate and Measure Capacity

CA Standards
MG 1.1, MG1.4

How many cups are in 2 pints?

There are 2 cups in each pint.

2 pints = 2 × 2 cups

Solution: There are 4 cups in 2 pints.

1 pint (pt) = 2 cups (c)
1 quart (qt) = 2 pints
1 gallon (gal) = 4 quarts

Find the missing amount. Use the chart for help.

1. 1 qt = _____ pt   2. 1 gal = _____ qt   3. 1 qt = _____ c

4. 1 gal = _____ pt   5. 2 gal = _____ pt   6. 2 pt = _____ c

7. 2 gal = _____ qt   8. 2 qt = _____ pt   9. 3 qt = _____ c

10. 4 pt = _____ c   11. 3 gal = _____ qt

Spiral Review   (Chapter 26, Lesson 2) **NS 2.5**

Divide. Check your answers.

12. 5)‾2‾1‾0‾ _____

13. 32)‾2‾8‾8‾ _____

14. Lakeview Elementary has 304 students in the third grade.
There are 16 third-grade classes, with the same number of
students in each class. How many students are
in each class? _____

Hands On: Estimate and Measure Capacity

CA Standards
MG 1.1, MG 1.4

For Problems 1–4, use the labeled capacity in each pair of containers to estimate the capacity of the unlabeled container in the pair. Then solve Problems 5–6.

1. About how many cups of hot chocolate will fill the large mug?

   1 cup

_____

2. About how many pints of yogurt are in the small carton?

    4 pints

_____

3. About many quarts of milk are in the small jug?

   5 quarts

_____

4. About how many gallons of water will fill the large cooler bottle?

   $\frac{1}{2}$ gallon

_____

5. Which container above has a capacity of 1 pint?

_____

6. Which container above has the greatest capacity? Which container above has the least capacity?

_____

Customary Units of Capacity

Choose the best unit to use for the container.
Write *cup*, *pint*, *quart*, or *gallon*.

Solution: A mug could not hold a pint,
a quart, or a gallon. The best unit to
measure the capacity of the mug is *cup*.

| 1 pint = 2 cups |
| 1 quart = 2 pints |
| 1 gallon = 4 quarts |

Choose the best unit to use for the container. Write *cup*, *pint*,
quart, or *gallon*.

1.  2 pints

_____

2. 2 cups

_____

Choose the better estimate.

3. tea pot

   a. 1 cup   **b.** 1 pint

4. paint can

   a. 1 gallon   **b.** 1 cup

Spiral Review   (Chapter 22, Lesson 4) **KEY** SDAP 1.3, MR 2.3

5. Make a vertical bar graph to show the data in the table.

   Use a 10 × 10 grid. _____

6. What is an appropriate scale to use for the data?

_____

7. Suppose 3 students switch from Chocolate to
Strawberry. How will this change affect the
bar graph?

Favorite Ice Cream	Number of Students
Vanilla	10
Chocolate	14
Strawberry	7
Other	4

_____

_____

_____

Customary Units of Capacity

Jennifer used the recipes below to make drinks for her party.
Use the recipes to solve each problem.

Berry Shake

Mix in a blender:
2 cups plain yogurt
2 teaspoons vanilla extract
3 cups frozen raspberries, thawed
1 pint strawberry ice cream

Fruit Punch

Mix in large punchbowl:
1 gallon orange juice
2 quarts pineapple juice
6 pints lime sherbet
1 quart ginger ale

1. How many pints of plain yogurt did Jennifer use for the berry shake?

_____

2. How many cups of ginger ale did Jennifer use for the fruit punch?

_____

3. Did Jennifer use more pineapple juice or lime sherbet in the punch? How many pints more?

_____

_____

4. Jennifer used the same amount of 2 ingredients to make the shakes. Which ingredients are they?

_____

_____

5. The difference between these two punch ingredient amounts is 6 pints. What are the ingredients?

_____

_____

6. Jennifer decides to make only half as much fruit punch. How many cups of juice (pineapple and orange) will she need?

_____

Hands On: Estimate and Measure Weight

CA Standards
MG 1.1, MG 1.0

Does the object below weigh more or less than 1 pound?

Customary Units of Weight

1 pound = 16 ounces

Solution: The object weighs *more* than 1 pound.

Estimate the weight of each object. Write *more* or *less* than 1 pound.

1.

2.

3.

4.

_____ _____ _____ _____

5.

6.

7.

8.

_____ _____ _____ _____

Spiral Review (Chapter 22, Lesson 5) **KEY** SDAP 1.3, MR 1.0

9. Construct a bar graph or a pictograph for the data.

10. What is an appropriate scale to use for your graph?

_____

11. Would a line graph be a good way to display the data? Explain.

_____

Favorite Food	Number of Students
Hamburger	12
French fries	5
Ice cream	9
Pizza	11

Hands On: Estimate and Measure Weight

CA Standards
MG 1.1, MG 1.0

Solve.

1. Katie reads the scale and it says 18 ounces. Is this more or less than one pound? How do you know?

   _____

   _____

2. Katie is recording the weight of a pencil. Should she use ounces or pounds? Explain.

   _____

   _____

3. Kyle is packing notebooks in a suitcase. The suitcase can weigh no more than 75 pounds. About how many notebooks will Kyle be able to pack in the suitcase?

   _____

4. Kyle is trying to determine the weight of a blender. What is a good estimate for the weight of a blender?

   _____

   _____

5. Katie is at a unique fruit stand. Every fruit costs the same amount, $1.50 per pound. About how much does a whole watermelon cost?

   _____

   _____

6. What is the difference in price between 12 lemons and 2 water melons?

   _____

   _____

Name _____ Date _____

Customary Units of Weight

CA Standards
MG 1.1, MG 1.0

What unit would you use to measure the weight of a desk?

Solution: Ounces would be too light. The best unit to measure the weight of the desk is *pounds*.

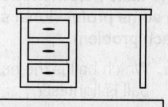

1 pound = 16 ounces

Choose the unit you would use to measure the weight.
Write *ounce* or *pound*.

1.

_____

2.

_____

3. lemon _____

4. cat _____

5. bicycle _____

6. shoe _____

Write in order from the least weight to the greatest weight.

7. 12 ounces 18 ounces 1 pound

8. 24 ounces 2 pounds 36 ounces

_____

_____

Spiral Review (Chapter 25, Lesson 2 and Chapter 26, Lesson 2) **NS 2.5**

Divide. Check your answers.

9. $11\overline{)440}$ _____

10. $35\overline{)245}$ _____

11. Hillside Bakery equally packs 1,240 cookies into 31 boxes. How many cookies are packed into each box? _____

Name _____ Date _____

Customary Units of Weight

CA Standards
MG 1.1, MG 1.0

The table below shows the normal weight of balls used in some professional sports. Use the table to solve each problem.

Professional Sports Balls	
Sport	**Ball Weight**
Baseball	5 ounces
Basketball	22 ounces
Bowling	96 ounces
Cricket	6 ounces
Golf	1 ounce
Rugby	15 ounces
Tennis	2 ounces
Volleyball	10 ounces

1. Which ball is the heaviest? Which ball is lightest?

   _____

2. Which balls weigh more than 1 pound?

   _____

   _____

3. Which sports' balls weigh less than $\frac{1}{2}$ pound?

   _____

   _____

4. You place a rugby ball on one pan of a balance scale. How many baseballs should you place on the other pan to balance the scale?

   _____

5. List all the pairs of balls for which the combined weight of the two balls is 1 pound.

   _____

   _____

6. The coach at Mountain Creek School purchased 16 baseballs, 10 basketballs, 4 bowling balls, 20 golf balls, and 40 tennis balls. What is the total weight of the purchase (in ounces)?

   _____

Convert Customary Units and Units of Time

CA Standards
AF 1.4, MG 1.4

Jessica worked for 7 hours. How many minutes did she work?

Solution:

There are 60 minutes in each hour, so Jessica worked 7 × 60 = 420 minutes.

Time	Length	Weight
1 minute = 60 seconds	1 foot = 12 inches	1 pound = 16 ounces
1 hour = 60 minutes	1 yard = 3 feet	
1 day = 24 hours	1 yard = 36 inches	
1 week = 7 days	1 mile = 5,280 feet	
1 year = 12 months		

Choose the expression you would use to find each. Then write the product or quotient.

1. number of weeks in 49 days

2. number of ounces in 3 pounds

3. number of pints in 4 gallons

4. number of minutes in 4 hours

5. number of days in 72 hours

6. number of cups in 15 pints

Spiral Review (Chapter 26, Lessons 2–4) **KEY** NS 2.3, NS 2.5, NS 2.7, **KEY** NS 3.3

Divide. Check your answers.

7. $345\overline{)1,725}$ _____

8. $455\overline{)5,460}$ _____

9. Tommy bought a pack of 12 golf balls for $46.20.

What is the price per ball? _____

Convert Customary Units and Units of Time

CA Standards
AF 1.4, MG 1.4

Solve.

1. Charlie's house is 2 miles away from school. What is the distance in feet?

   _____

2. Kevin is going on vacation in 4 weeks. How many days is 4 weeks?

   _____

3. Jack's pail has 4 pints of water in it. Ayana's pail has 10 cups. Whose pail has more water in it? How do you know?

   _____

   _____

   _____

4. Maria blinks at least once per minute. How many times does she blink in a year?

   _____

5. Chicken noodle soup costs $3 per cup. What is the price of 4 quarts of chicken noodle soup?

   _____

6. Fiona has 63 yards of fabric to make skirts. If each skirt requires 40 inches of material, how many skirts can Fiona make?

   _____

Name _____ Date _____

Unit Costs

CA Standards
MR 2.4, NS 2.7

A 10-ounce bag of potting soil costs $2.40. A 3-pound bag of potting soil costs $7.20. Which bag has a greater unit cost?

Step 1 First, you need to convert one of the units. There are 16 ounces in 1 pound, so there are 48 ounces in 3 pounds of potting soil.

Step 2 Find the unit costs. For the 10-ounce bag, divide $2.40 by 10 ounces to get $0.24 per ounce. For the 3-pound bag, divide $7.20 by 48 ounces to get $0.15 per ounce.

Step 3 Now compare the unit costs.

$0.24 per ounce > $0.15 per ounce, so the 10-ounce bag has a greater unit cost.

1. At one store, Haley found milk selling for $1.09 per quart. Another store was selling gallons of milk for $3.56 each. How do the unit prices compare?

_____

_____

2. A half dozen hair clips cost $3.90. Maria wants to buy 4 hair clips. How much will she pay for them? _____

Spiral Review (Chapter 26, Lessons 2-3) **KEY** NS 2.5, NS 2.7, **KEY** NS 3.3

Solve.

3. A store sells 3 jars of paste for $5.79 and 5 pads of sticky notes for $4.50. What is the total cost of 1 jar of paste and 3 pads of sticky notes? _____

4. A mug costs $3.85, and a cereal bowl costs $2.55. How much do 4 mugs and 2 cereal bowls cost in all? _____

Unit Costs

CA Standards
MR 2.4, NS 2.7

Solve. Explain why your answer makes sense.

1. Mrs. Rothenberg bought a bag of 6 pears for $5.40. What was the unit price per pear?

2. A package of 4 buttons costs $1.30. How much will 4 packages cost?

3. A bag of 6 doughnuts costs $5.10. A bag of 8 doughnuts costs $6.56. Which bag has the lower unit cost?

4. A box of cereal contains 18 ounces and costs $4.14. A 1-pound box of cereal costs $4.00. Which box has the lower unit cost?

5. Mr. Cavarro spent $36.96 filling his car's gas tank with 16 gallons of gas. Ms. Loring spent $30.94 for 14 gallons of gas at a different gas station. How much did each person spend per gallon?

6. Julie bought 3 pints of orange juice for $4.17. Kris bought a quart of orange juice for $1.89. Lonnie bought a gallon of orange juice for $4.99. What was the unit cost per pint that each person paid?

Hands On: Metric Units of Capacity

**Which is the better estimate for the capacity of a coffee cup?
200 mL or 200 L**

This water bottle holds 1 liter
of water.

The dropper holds 1 milliliter
of liquid.

Solution: The better estimate for the capacity of a coffee cup is 200 mL

Choose the better estimate for the capacity of each.

1.

2 L or 20 L

2.

1 L or 4 L

3.

10 L or 10 mL

**Choose the unit you would use to measure the capacity of
each. Write *mL* or *L*.**

4. a juice box

_____

5. a measuring cup

_____

6. a sink

_____

Spiral Review (Chapter 26, Lesson 2) **NS 2.5**

7. 336 ÷ 3 = _____

8. 995 ÷ 5 = _____

9. Eduardo has 264 vintage baseball cards. He needs special plastic sheets to
protect his cards. The plastic sheets can only fit 6 cards per sheet. How many

sheets does Eduardo need for his baseball cards? _____

Name _____ Date _____

Hands On: Metric Units of Capacity

Solve each problem.

1. Teddy was asked to wash his father's car. He filled his bucket with 12 liters of water. How many milliliters of water does Teddy's bucket have?

   _____

2. Teddy added 1,000 milliliters of detergent to his bucket of water? How many liters did Teddy add?

   _____

3. Stevie gives his horse 5,000 milliliters of water a day. How many liters of water does Stevie's horse get each week?

   _____

   _____

4. Daniela had to drink 2 L of a special juice each day for three days in a row. How many milliliters did Daniela drink in 3 days?

   _____

   _____

5. Every Thursday, two jugs of water, which contain 10,000 milliliters each, are delivered to Elvia's house. How many liters of water did Elvia receive in 4 weeks worth of deliveries?

   _____

   _____

6. Tony has a fish tank that can hold 11 L of water. Robert has two fish tanks, one that holds 5,000 milliliters of water and one that holds 5 liters of water. Whose tank(s) can hold the greatest milliliters of water? How many milliliters does this tank(s) hold?

   _____

   _____

   _____

Hands On: Metric Units of Mass

CA Standard
MG 1.1

Which is the better estimate for the mass of a CD? 10 g or 10 kg

A peanut has a mass of about
1 gram.

A baking potato has a mass of about
300 grams.

A cauliflower head has a mass of
about 1 kilogram.

1 kilogram = 1,000 grams

Solution: The better estimate for the mass of a CD is 10 g.

Choose the unit you would use to measure the mass of each.
Write *g* or *kg*.

1. a pen

2. a couch

3. an orange

_____ _____ _____

Choose the better estimate.

4. a dog

5. a steel doorstop

6. a feather

3 kg or 30 kg _____

70 kg or 7 kg _____

1 g or 100 g _____

Spiral Review (Chapter 26, Lesson 2) **NS 2.5, MR 2.2**

7. 4,648 ÷ 7 = _____

8. $333.81 ÷ 3 = _____

9. Brenda had 4,100 pennies. She took them to her local bank
to exchange them for paper money. How much money did
Brenda receive from the bank for her pennies?

_____

Hands On: Metric Units of Mass

CA Standard
MG 1.1

River dolphins live in muddy rivers of South America and Asia. Most are much smaller than their more familiar cousins, the ocean dolphins.

Use the table to solve each problem. Show your work.

1. Which calf has a mass equal to 4 kilograms?

_____

_____

2. Which adult dolphin has a mass of 40,000 grams?

_____

_____

River Dolphins		
Dolphin	**Calf Mass**	**Adult Mass**
Amazon	7 kg	120 kg
Chinese	4,000 g	130 kg
Franciscana	8 kg	40 kg
Ganges	7,500 g	80 kg

3. Which adult dolphin has twice the mass of the Franciscana?

_____

_____

4. Which calf has 4,000 grams more mass than the Chinese calf?

_____

_____

5. Which dolphin calf would be equal in mass to the Franciscana and twice that of the Chinese if 500 grams were added to its mass?

_____

_____

_____

6. For which two dolphin calves is the difference in their masses 3 kilograms?

_____

_____

_____

Convert Metric Units

Convert the unit by choosing the right expression.

Erica has 4 liters of water in her beach pail. Which expression would she use to find how many milliliters are in 4 liters?

$$4 \times 1{,}000 = 4{,}000 \text{ mL}$$
OR
$$1{,}000 \div 4 = 250 \text{ mL}$$

Solution: Erica would use $4 \times 1{,}000 = 4{,}000$ mL, because there are 1,000 mL in 1 liter.

**Choose the expression you would use to convert the units.
Then convert the units.**

1. the number of centimeters in 20 meters

   a. 20×100 **b.** $100 \div 20$

   _____

2. the number of milliliters in 10 liters

   a. $1{,}000 \div 10$ **b.** $10 \times 1{,}000$

   _____

3. the number of meters in 800 centimeters

   a. 800×100 **b.** $800 \div 100$

   _____

4. the number of kilograms in 6,000 grams

   a. $6{,}000 \times 1{,}000$ **b.** $6{,}000 \div 1{,}000$

   _____

5. the number of liters in 4,000 milliliters

   a. $4{,}000 \times 1{,}000$ **b.** $4{,}000 \div 1{,}000$

   _____

6. the number of grams in 8 kilograms

   a. $1{,}000 \div 8$ **b.** $8 \times 1{,}000$

   _____

Spiral Review   (Chapter 27, Lessons 1 and 2) **AF 2.1**

7. 2 gal = _____ pt

8. Choose the better estimate for the mass of a wrist watch.

   a. 3 oz   **b.** 3 lb

9. Golda's mother was asked to donate 24 quarts of apple juice for Golda's third-grade picnic. How many gallons of apple juice is that?

   _____

Convert Metric Units of Capacity and Mass

CA Standards
AF 1.4, **KEY** AF 2.1, MG 1.0

Solve each problem by choosing the right expression to convert the units. Show your work.

1. Amy had 12 meters of rope to tie her dog, Rex, to the fence post. How many centimeters of rope did Amy have?

_____

_____

2. Peter grew a pumpkin for the county fair that had a mass of 12,000 grams. What is the mass of Peter's pumpkin in kilograms?

_____

_____

3. Rosa and Tamika both have wading pools. Rosa's pool can hold 8 L of water. Tamika's can hold 1,000 milliliters more than Rosa's. How many milliliters of water can Tamika's pool hold?

_____

_____

4. Tom bought new sneakers that had a mass of 1,000 grams more than his old sneakers. His old sneakers had a mass of 1 kilogram. What is the mass in kilograms of Tom's new sneakers?

_____

_____

5. Ali decided to paint his tree house. He bought 1,000 milliliters of red paint for the roof. Then he bought 1,000 milliliters of blue paint for the rest of the sides. When he ran out of blue paint, he bought 1 more liter. How many liters of paint did Ali buy in all?

_____

_____

6. Tom's new sneakers were made for basketball. His old sneakers were for playing tennis and had shoelaces that were 50 centimeters each. Both shoelaces on his new basketball shoes equal the total amount of his old tennis shoes, plus 100 centimeters. How many meters end-to-end are Tom's basketball shoelaces?

_____

_____